PRAEGER LIBRARY OF U.S. GOVERNMENT
DEPARTMENTS AND AGENCIES

The National Science Foundation

PRAEGER LIBRARY OF U.S. GOVERNMENT DEPARTMENTS
AND AGENCIES

Consulting Editors

ERNEST S. GRIFFITH

Former University Professor and Dean Emeritus, School of International Service, American University; former Director, Legislative Reference Service, Library of Congress; and author of *The American System of Government* and *The Modern Government in Action.*

HUGH LANGDON ELSBREE

Former Chairman, Department of Political Science, Dartmouth College; former Managing Editor, *American Political Science Review;* former Director, Legislative Reference Service, Library of Congress.

The National Science Foundation

Dorothy Schaffter

FREDERICK A. PRAEGER, *Publishers*
New York · Washington · London

FREDERICK A. PRAEGER, *Publishers*
111 Fourth Avenue, New York, N.Y. 10003, U.S.A.
5, Cromwell Place, London S.W.7, England

Published in the United States of America in 1969
by Frederick A. Praeger, Inc., Publishers

Library of Congress Catalog Card Number: 68–8137

This book is No. 16 in the series
Praeger Library of U.S. Government Departments and Agencies

Printed in the United States of America

In memory of my mother,
HATTIE SCHAFFTER

Preface

After Henry James had finished his novel *The Tragic Muse,* he wrote, "I took long and patient and careful trouble which no creature will recognize." Now that I have completed this book on the National Science Foundation, I understand how he felt. But, alas, James Thurber's often quoted "This book tells me more about penguins than I wish to know" also comes to mind. After all the hard work, have I merely committed overkill?

I do not doubt the importance of my subject. There is much to be said about this relatively small, comparatively new agency. The Foundation is now about eighteen years old. Will it live to be as old as the four original departments of the U.S. Government—State, Treasury, Army, and Justice? Will it grow into a major department? Will it be broken up, with its various parts transferred to other departments? Will it become one part of a new "department of science"? The Foundation's annual budget averages less than a half-billion dollars, making it seem insignificant in the great federal structure of major departments and independent agencies with total expenditures of many billions of dollars. Were the hopes and aims of its founders extravagant, or are they on the way to achievement?

I have been privileged to witness the entire career of the Foundation from the vantage point of a senior specialist in American government and public administration in the Legislative Reference Service of the Library of Congress, beginning in the period immediately after World War II. Until 1964, I was involved at all times in the study of the rapidly expanding government organization for the federal support of scientific research and development, including, of course, the establishment and career of the National Science Foundation. The problems that Congress, the executive branch, and the so-called scientific community face in working together are primarily problems of political science and public administration, not of physics or chemistry or biology. It is from the political scientist's point of view that I have approached this book. I can only hope that the continuous contact I have had with the federal programs in support of science will be sufficient to justify my authorship.

Because, in a sense, I started to work on this book so many years ago, it is difficult for me to acknowledge all the sources of the assistance I received. These include, particularly, the two men who are presently the consulting editors of the Praeger Library of U.S. Government Departments and Agencies—Dr. Ernest S. Griffith and Dr. Hugh Langdon Elsbree, both of them directors of the Legislative Reference Service during my tour of duty. If I were to name all my colleagues in the Service with whom I worked on studies of federal support of science, I would have a long list. Failure to name them does not signify lack of appreciation. They all helped me to realize this book, and I hope they find it worthy.

DOROTHY SCHAFFTER

Washington, D.C.
April, 1969

Contents

ix

List of Tables

A National Science Foundation organization chart appears on pages 24–25.

A section of photographs follows page 84.

The National Science Foundation

I

Origins, Historic and Legislative

The National Science Foundation (NSF), generally considered to have had a successful career since its establishment in 1950, is the product of history starting long before. Because the NSF formalizes certain aspects of the relationship between federal government and science, it cannot be understood as an organization without considering that relationship. The classic work on this subject is A. Hunter Dupree's *Science in the Federal Government: A History of Policies and Activities to 1940,* which describes the relations between the federal government and science from 1787 until the beginning of the specific movement to create the kind of agency established in 1950. We can look only at the highlights of this period.

BEFORE THE CIVIL WAR

During the Constitutional Convention of 1787, a few suggestions were made and debated concerning the role the federal government might play in promotion of science. No specific provision appeared in the final document, although there were grants of authority over the census, patents, and standards of weights and measures. The more general powers of Congress over common defense, general welfare, and the regulation of interstate commerce, as it turned out when the new government was in operation, were the chief sources of legislative action in support of science.

Before the Civil War, there were such government-supported scientific activities as the Lewis and Clark expedition and the various surveys made by the Coast and Geodetic Survey, the

3

U.S. Army Corps of Engineers, and the U.S. Military Academy. There also was the establishment, in 1846, of the Smithsonian Institution, that odd mixture of private and public endeavor.

By the middle of the nineteenth century, scientists were becoming a specialized professional group. During the Civil War, the Navy began to use their advice. But of greatest significance in those years was the establishment by Congress in 1863 of the National Academy of Sciences, a body of scientists who were available to all government agencies on request.

To World War I

The Department of Agriculture, the first and largest of the permanent scientific agencies created by Congress (in 1862), was given Cabinet status in 1889. Acting under the Homestead and Morrill Acts of 1862, the department organized a number of bureaus to carry on research in specialized fields such as plant and animal husbandry. The Hatch Act of 1887 instituted support for the agricultural experiment stations, which had grown up around the land grant colleges, and federal funds began to be used not only by federal agencies but also to sponsor research in state institutions. This use is the oldest surviving example of a type of support now furnished throughout the federal scientific program.

Next came a number of scientifically oriented agencies— the National Bureau of Standards (1901), the U.S. Public Health Service (1912), and the National Advisory Committee for Aeronautics (1915). Through the period between the Civil War and the outbreak of World War I, according to J. Stefan Dupré and Sanford A. Lakoff in *Science and the Nation: Policy and Politics*:

> In all federal programs . . . science was regarded not as a thing apart, valuable in itself, but always and only as a tool for the solution of problems and the formulation of policy. . . .
> Yet science had a wide-ranging impact on government apart from any immediate usefulness. Through regulation, it frequently provided the lead in the growing interrelation of the public and pri-

vate sectors of the economy. Equally important, the need for well-qualified scientists was one of the key factors in the gradual replacement of political patronage by a civil service merit system.

World War I led to several new developments. In 1915, the U.S. Navy established under Thomas Edison its Naval Consulting Board, consisting of a number of specialized scientific committees used in a general advisory capacity. This board was the basis for the permanent Naval Research Laboratory created after the war. The National Academy of Sciences, which had been relatively inactive, now urged greater use of scientists by the government, and President Woodrow Wilson created the National Research Council (NRC), which was closely related to the National Academy. After January, 1918, the NRC, acting with certain divisions of the armed services, the Bureau of Mines, and the Bureau of Standards, carried out research projects in such areas as gas warfare and optics. Close relationships were established with the chemical and optical industries; the universities also contributed personnel and performed research at the government's request.

THE 1920's AND 1930's

Dupré and Lakoff say the following about the 1920's:

> . . . the decade . . . saw little in the development of government science. The NRC, while given permanent status, languished for lack of funds, and Armed Forces appropriations were cut to the bone. America "kept cool" with Coolidge, laissez-faire was restored in its full purity, and science was relegated to the proverbial ivory tower. Among high officials, only Herbert Hoover showed much interest in the scientific establishment, but his efforts to create a National Research Fund for pure science from business contributions proved a failure.

Not until the 1930's and the administration of Franklin D. Roosevelt was there any acceleration in the kind of thought that would alter policy and eventually suggest the creation of a national science agency. A Presidential Science Advisory Board was created in 1933 to investigate the use of science by government agencies. Between 1938 and 1941, the National Resources Committee published a three-volume report, *Research—A National Resource,* which surveyed scientific activity in government, industry, and the universities. The committee recommended that the federal government establish closer relations with scientists and sponsor more research within the government and outside it.

By 1940, shortly before the United States entered World War II, no striking changes had been made. Most government agencies continued to use science only as a tool, and the federal budget for science was only about $75 million.

During World War II

The real revolution in the relationship of the government and science came during World War II. In 1940,. President Roosevelt, aware that the United States might soon be involved in the fighting, established the National Defense Research Committee (NRC) to encourage scientific research in weaponry. It received generous funds, and its membership consisted of Vannevar Bush, president of the Carnegie Institution, as chairman, the presidents of Harvard and MIT, the U.S. Commissioner of Patents, the president of Bell Telephone Laboratories, a general, an admiral, and two university scientists.

The following year, the President created a new agency and attached it to the Executive Office. This was the famous Office of Scientific Research and Development (OSRD), with Vannevar Bush as head. The OSRD was a clearinghouse for much of the research and development of other government agencies, including the NDRC. It could initiate projects of its own, and it was the center for the mobilization of scientific manpower. The OSRD began the atomic energy research project, which it later turned over to the Army's Manhattan Project.

With science now located at the highest level, in the office of the President, scientific advisory committees multiplied, bringing almost the entire scientific community into close cooperation with government in one way or another. The U.S.

Government's contract authority was used to set up entire research centers, federally financed but administered by industry and universities—for example, the Los Alamos Laboratory, set up under an Army contract with the University of California. Wartime scientific developments were large and expensive, indicating that peacetime financing of research was going to be costly. The scientific community, alarmed because all existing basic research results had been utilized in the developments of the war period, campaigned actively for increased support of basic research in the national interest.

The culmination of the World War II period was a report to President Harry S Truman by Vannevar Bush entitled *Science: The Endless Frontier*. This classic work contained the first official and authoritative proposals for a national science foundation. A chapter called "The Means to the End" recommended that the federal government accept "new responsibilities for promoting the creation of new scientific knowledge and the development of scientific talent in our youth" and said that, in discharging these responsibilities, federal funds should be made available. The essential point made in the chapter was the following:

> There should be a focal point within the Government for a concerted program of assisting scientific research conducted outside of Government. Such an agency should furnish the funds needed to support basic research in the colleges and universities, should coordinate where possible research programs on matters of utmost importance to the national welfare, should formulate a national policy for the Government toward science, should sponsor the interchange of scientific information among scientists and laboratories both in this country and abroad, and should ensure that the incentives to research in industry and the universities are maintained. All of the committees advising on these matters agree on the necessity for such an agency.

There followed a brief description of the activities of many groups in government departments concerned "with science as collateral and peripheral" to their major problems, noting that these groups should remain where they were and continue to perform their present functions. They could not be made the repository of the new and large responsibilities in science, which belonged to the government and which the government should accept. The proposal continued:

> A new agency should be established, therefore, by the Congress for the purpose. Such an agency, moreover, should be an independent agency devoted to the support of scientific research and advanced scientific education alone. Industry learned many years ago that basic research cannot often be fruitfully conducted as an adjunct to or a subdivision of an operating agency or department. Operating agencies have immediate operating goals and are under constant pressure to produce in a tangible way, for that is the test of their value. None of these conditions is favorable to basic research. Research is the exploration of the unknown and is necessarily speculative. It is inhibited by conventional approaches, traditions, and standards. It cannot be satisfactorily conducted in an atmosphere where it is gauged and tested by operating or production standards. Basic scientific research should not, therefore, be placed under an operating agency whose paramount concern is anything other than research. Research will always suffer when put in competition with operations.

Bush's statement of the five principles he believed must underlie the proposed new agency and his detailed suggestions for a "national research foundation"—its purposes, members, organization, functions, patent policy, special authority, budget, and action by Congress—are remarkable for their practicality and farsightedness, especially when one recalls that they were made five years before the National Science Foundation was created by Congress in 1950. Fundamentally, today's organization is in line with the Bush proposals, although many provisions concerning organization, function, and powers differ.

POSTWAR PRESSURES

In the immediate post–World War II years, two other important advisory groups recommended the establishment of a national science agency. In 1947, the President's Scientific

Research Board, under the chairmanship of John R. Steelman, published a five-volume report under the general title *Science and Public Policy.* The first volume, *A Program for the Nation,* contained brief statements relating to the establishment of a national science foundation. The Steelman board recommended:

> That a National Science Foundation be established to make grants in support of basic research, with a Director appointed by and responsible to the President. The Director should be advised by a part-time board of eminent scientists and educators, half to be drawn from outside the Federal Government and half from within it.
>
> That a Federal program of assistance to undergraduate and graduate students in the sciences be developed as an integral part of an over-all national scholarship and fellowship program.
>
> That a program of Federal assistance to universities and colleges be developed in the matters of laboratory facilities and scientific equipment as an integral part of a general program of aid to education.

The first Hoover Commission, in its report of March, 1949, on federal research, urged the establishment of a national science foundation, basing its recommendations largely on the recently published studies of the Steelman board. The commission's statement was brief, calling for the continuation of staff organizations in federal agencies with extensive research programs but concluding that efforts along these lines in individual agencies were not enough. Even an interdepartmental committee such as the one created by executive order in December, 1947, was held to be insufficient. The major functions of the kind of agency the commission recommended would be:

> (a) to examine the total scientific research effort of the Nation, (b) to assess the proper role of the Federal Government in this effort, (c) to evaluate the division of research effort among the scientific disciplines and among fields of applied research, and (d) to evaluate the key factors that impede the development of an effective national research effort. Based upon its investiga-

tions, it should advise the President as to the measures necessary to establish a sound scientific research program for the Nation.

Notice should be taken of one development of great importance late in the 1940's. Of this event, Luther J. Carter, in an article in *Science* (July 23, 1966), wrote:

> Nearly 20 years ago, on August 1, 1946, the Office of Naval Research [ONR] finally came into being, to the immense satisfaction of the true believers who had been insisting that just such an agency would be a vital necessity in the postwar years. ONR, authorized to support the basic research of university scientists as well as to lead the Navy's "in-house" research, was the first agency to take up, on a broad scale, the challenge laid down . . . by Vannevar Bush. . . .
>
> Well before the end of World War II it was realized that, with the return of peace, the Office of Scientific Research and Development and the National Defense Research Committee, both temporary wartime bodies, would disappear. Unless a new agency came to the scene, government support of science would falter. As things developed, for a few years ONR filled the void.

Secretary of the Navy James Forrestal and other important Navy figures arranged to have certain unused wartime funds transferred to the ONR, and Bush and other scientists helped to create a favorable political climate, enabling the ONR to start a program of basic research. The ONR's first chief scientist became the first director of the National Science Foundation in 1950. The research-contract methods developed and used successfully by the ONR later served as models for the NSF and other research-supporting agencies.

The Legal Basis of the National Science Foundation

The legislative history of the Foundation began on July 19, 1945, when the first two of many proposed bills for its establishment were introduced by Senator Warren G. Magnuson and Representative Wilbur Mills. The two bills followed Bush's recommendations for a national research foundation.

Later bills, in which the phrase "national science foundation" came to be used, modified many provisions of the measures introduced in 1945. During the five years, there was a continuous effort to write legislation creating a permanent government agency with the necessary functions and powers for fostering American science—an effort that turned out to be filled with difficulties. Several different bills were considered before one (S.526) was finally passed in 1947. Although President Truman strongly favored establishment of the Foundation, he vetoed this measure, on August 6, 1947, because so much authority was vested in a part-time board that it appeared to violate the President's constitutional authority. The board, which was to have determined vital national policies and expended large public funds, would have been essentially a group of individual private citizens. In the President's judgment, this provision constituted a marked departure from sound principles of public administration. Truman strongly favored establishment of the Foundation. New bills to correct these objections were introduced in 1948 and again in 1949. Although 150 leading authorities in science, education, and medicine had presented over 1,200 pages of testimony in the preceding years, new hearings were held.

Finally, Congress passed an amended version of the bill introduced on January 6, 1949 (S.247), and it was approved by President Truman on May 10, 1950, as the National Science Foundation Act of 1950 (Public Law 81-507). In approving the measure, Truman stated that the establishment of the Foundation was a major landmark in the history of science in the United States. During the postwar years, the world had not found peacetime security, and this fact underscored the need for the Foundation. The President stressed the necessity for the United States to maintain its leadership in scientific progress and said that the Foundation, stimulating basic research and education in science, would add to the supply of knowledge indispensable to the continued growth, prosperity, and security of the country. He urged that the Foundation's work have the complete support of the American people.

The Foundation was established in the first paragraph of the first section of the act in these words: "There is established in the executive branch of the government an independent agency to be known as the National Science Foundation. . . . The Foundation shall consist of a National Science Board . . . and a director."

This act, with later amendments, is the basic law today. There have been several amendments by acts of Congress, by reorganization plans, and by executive orders of the President, but they have not greatly altered the authority of the Foundation. Additional acts of Congress and executive orders not relating primarily to the Foundation and not included in Chapter 16, Title 42 (USC), have in many instances contained provisions relating to the Foundation.

Here is a list of the contents of Chapter 16:

Establishment of National Science Foundation
Functions of the Foundation
National Science Board
Director of the Foundation
Power of board to create committees
Divisions within Foundation
Divisional committees
Special commissions
Scholarships and graduate fellowships
General authority of Foundation
Patent rights
International cooperation and coordination with foreign
    policy
Weather modification
Employment of personnel
Security provisions
Appropriations
Science Information Service
Science Information Council
Functions relating to Science Information Service and
    Council

Appropriations for Science Information Service and Council
National Medal of Science
Same: award, number, citizenship, ceremonies

Since the publication of the 1964 edition of the U.S. Code,
two items have been added to those in Title 42, Chapter 16.
Both are printed in Volume II of Supplement II, 1965–66, to
the 1964 Code:

> *U.S.C. Title 42, Chapter 16 (sections 1864 and 1867) Reorganization Plan No. 5 of 1965*
> > Director of the Foundation; appointment; tenure; powers and
> > duties.
> > Divisional committees; composition; terms of office; chairmen; rules; duties; recommendations.
> *U.S.C. Title 33, Chapter 22. Sea grant colleges and marine science development*
> > Subchapter I. Marine resources and engineering development,
> > Congressional declaration of policy and objectives.
> > Subchapter II. Sea grant colleges.

II

The Broad Purposes

What does the National Science Foundation do? A great deal has been said about what the National Science Foundation should do, but many questions involved have not been answered finally. They cannot be answered without raising other broad questions about the structure of science activities of all federal agencies, colleges and universities, industry, nonprofit foundations, and individual scientists and students. This is far too large a subject to be discussed thoroughly here, although it must be taken into consideration. We can say what the NSF actually does, although even that is complicated.

The act of 1950 describes the functions of the Foundation, which are:

1. to develop and encourage the pursuit of a national policy for the promotion of basic research and education in the sciences;

2. to initiate and support basic scientific research and programs to strengthen scientific research potential in the mathematical, physical, medical, biological, engineering, and other sciences, by making contracts or other arrangements (including grants, loans, and other forms of assistance) to support such scientific activities and to appraise the impact of research upon industrial development and upon the general welfare;

3. at the request of the Secretary of Defense, to initiate and support specific scientific research activities in connection with with matters relating to the national defense by making contracts or other arrangements (including grants, loans, and other forms of assistance) for the conduct of such scientific research;

4. to award, as provided in section 1869 of this title, scholar-

ships and graduate fellowships in the mathematical, physical, medical, biological, engineering, and other sciences;

5. to foster the interchange of scientific information among scientists in the United States and foreign countries;

6. to evaluate scientific research programs undertaken by agencies of the Federal Government, and to correlate the Foundation's scientific research programs with those undertaken by individuals and by public and private research groups;

7. to establish such special commissions as the Board may from time to time deem necessary for the purposes of this chapter;

8. to maintain a register of scientific and technical personnel and in other ways provide a central clearinghouse for information covering all scientific and technical personnel in the United States, including its Territories and possessions;

9. to initiate and support a program of study, research, and evaluation in the field of weather modification, giving particular attention to areas that have experienced floods, drought, hail, lightning, fog, tornadoes, hurricanes, or other weather phenomena, and to report annually to the President and the Congress thereon.

A reading of the legal definition of the Foundation's functions, without any background information concerning developments and changes since 1945 when the first proposals for a foundation were made, gives the impression that its purposes are rather clearly spelled out. The Foundation is to support scientific research and scientific education through fellowships and grants and other methods and to develop national science policy and evaluate and correlate the science activities of the federal government.

However, Reorganization Plan No. 2 of 1962 amended the text of the original law by transferring from the Foundation to the director of the Office of Science and Technology (OST) as much of the functions described in paragraph (1) as would enable him to advise and assist the President in achieving coordinated federal policies for the promotion of basic research and education in the sciences. This reorganization plan also amended paragraph (6) by transferring from the Foundation to the director of the OST the function of evaluating scientific research programs undertaken by agencies of the federal government.

The support of research and education was immediately instituted by the Foundation after passage of the act of 1950, and programs to carry this purpose into effect have increased steadily in number and in size, and are generally considered to be successful. But development of policy and coordination of federal science activities proved far more difficult to achieve and, in fact, the Foundation has not become the principal federal agency for these purposes. By the early 1960's, it was apparent that the Foundation, for whatever reasons, was not developing federal science policy nor coordinating federal science activities. Hence, the Reorganization Act of 1962 established the Office of Science and Technology in the office of the President and transferred to that new agency most of the policy-making function of the NSF and all of its function of coordination.

This change left the Foundation the job of supporting— that is to say, funding—basic research through grants, fellowships, and other means, and this is what it continues to do. In addition to the programs described by the 1950 legislation— promoting basic research, science education, institutional support for science, science information activities, and so on— the Foundation also administers the Sea Grant College and Program Act (Public Law 89-688) of 1966.

What Might Have Been

It is useful at this point to review in brief some views of the role (intended or achieved) of the National Science Foundation as presented by well-qualified observers. In *Science* (May 6, 1960), Alan T. Waterman, director of the NSF from 1957–63, wrote of the functions assigned by the act of 1950:

In the first or operational category, planning and execution have been reasonably straightforward. . . .

The policy-making functions, as well as the evaluation functions prescribed in the act were less susceptible of immediate and specific action. . . .

In *Science—The Endless Frontier,* Bush had visualized that a National Research Foundation would be the principal, if not, indeed, the sole, point of reference for federal support of basic or uncommitted research in the postwar period. In view of the brilliant success of the wartime Office of Scientific Research and Development, this was a logical plan for taking care of the nation's research needs in science. So urgent were these needs, however, particularly in the mathematics, science, and engineering departments of universities, and so urgent was the nation's need for scientific research that the provision of federal support could not await the outcome of the 5-year congressional debate over legislation to establish the National Science Foundation.

When the National Science Foundation began to operate in 1951, initial policy had been formulated and active support of science was under way, and as a result there was pressing demand for (1) impartial support of basic research and training unrelated to such practical missions as defense and health and (2) supervision, coordination, and policy determination among the growing and splintered research-support programs of the federal government.

Equipped with a broad charter, a limited but growing staff, and an operating budget of $3.5 million, the new foundation found itself under pressure almost immediately to start performing policy-making and evaluation functions. In addition, of course, it was expected to launch, as early as possible, programs in support of basic research and education in the sciences.*

In 1965–66, the House Committee on Science and Astronautics undertook a thorough review of the operations and functions of the NSF. In a report entitled *The National Science Foundation: Its Present and Future,*† the committee stated:

Any idea that the Foundation exists without a central mission to give coherence and force to its operations is incorrect. The

* Copyright 1960 by the American Association for the Advancement of Science.

† Throughout this book, there are references to two reports resulting from the committee review. The first, *The National Science Foundation: Its Present and Future,* was House Report 1236 (1966). The second, entitled *The National Science Foundation: A General Review of Its First 15 Years,* was House Report 1219 (1966). References hereafter are shortened to House Report 1236 (1966) and House Report 1219 (1966).

eight functions set out in the National Science Foundation Act of 1950 comprise and outline a mission of great current and future importance, one that can affect the future of the country as dramatically as missions which leave more visible results, such as highways, dams and hospitals. . . .

This mission extends to and impacts upon the whole of the nation's scientific and engineering community wherever it is found: on campus, in industry and in government. . . . the Foundation has the potential to become a powerful instrument of national policy for science, shaping it, interacting with it, and helping to carry it forward.

Don K. Price, dean of the John Fitzgerald Kennedy School of Government, Harvard University, has been a student of the relations between science and government for many years. He has published books and articles on the subject and has appeared as a witness at many hearings before committees of Congress. In *Government and Science: Their Dynamic Relation in American Democracy*, Price describes the Foundation as "the only agency of government that can help the President and the Congress appraise the general policies of the government with respect to science." He wrote that "no other agency is in a position to look at the way in which all the specialized programs of the federal government affect science as a whole."

Discussing the different points of view concerning the proper relations between government and science at the time when establishment of the Foundation was under consideration, Price said that, at the end of the war, one group did not want to continue its power: "On the contrary, they wished to see the country adopt a system more suitable for the support of basic science and better adapted to the protection of science in peacetime from the threats of bureaucratic control or political interference."

Price continues:

On the other hand, some of those interested in the general problems of organization and administration in the government naturally started with a different point of view. They believed that the government would have to go into the support of science on an entirely new scale, and that such support would make the control of research and development an important key to many issues affecting powerful interests in society. For this reason they were mainly interested in seeing that the new federal agencies for the support of research should be organized in a responsible relation to the rest of the executive branch, and particularly to the President.

These two points of view were held by two groups of men with equal devotion to the public interest and to public service. The difference of opinion . . . grew naturally out of their different backgrounds and experience. One was primarily interested in maintaining the freedom of science, and the other in increasing the responsibility of the administration of government. . . .

I have oversimplified the problem by posing it as an issue between two sharply defined points of view. There were, of course, all sorts of variations, in part the result of normal differences in theory, in part the result of normal prejudices and selfish interests. In short, the problem was about as complicated as any other major political problem. But the issue of reconciling the objectivity and independence of science with the responsibility of the governmental system was the most important thread that ran through all the tangled argument.

In *The Scientific Estate,* Price summarizes the operational development of the National Science Foundation:

When Congress was considering its creation at the end of the Second World War, it was assumed (in both of the alternative versions of the bill) that the Foundation was to have responsibilities not only for basic research but for certain applied research programs as well, and that it was, moreover, to coordinate the basic research programs of the operating agencies. In the bill favored by the leadership of the Office of Scientific Research and Development, the Foundation was to be headed by a board of eminent private citizens, serving on a part-time basis, and with authority to appoint their own executive director. When President Truman objected to this formula, and the bill was held up, the War and Navy Departments sought to continue their wartime collaboration with scientists and en-

gineers from private institutions by setting up in the National
Academy of Sciences a Research Board for National Security,
which would have been in effect a continuation of the OSRD
program. That proposal was rejected; the weapons research
programs were picked up enthusiastically by the military services themselves; and when the Foundation was finally established its proposed function in applied research and development had been forgotten, but it was still assigned by law the
responsibility to coordinate the basic research programs of the
entire government.

In this role, the Foundation was a failure—or perhaps it
would be fairer to say that it was too realistic ever to try to
play the part. Its disappointed supporters were inclined to
attribute this failure to political prudence, maybe even cow-
ardice. . . . Managerial theorists were inclined to say that
the Foundation failed because it was not located in the Executive Office of the President. . . . Two other explanations seem
more cogent.

First, although the director of the Foundation was appointed
by the President, the highest formal authority in the Foundation
was still the National Science Board, made up of men on part-
time duty, nominated to the President by a variety of scientific
associations and institutions. The success of the director turned
on a delicate balance between his loyalties to this board, representing the scientific community, and to the President. In such a
relationship, neither he nor the chairman of the board was in a
position to be an effective full-time staff agent of the President,
or to work out the relationship of continual compromise with
other staff agencies, representing other types of interests and
concerns, in the President's Executive Office.

Second, the Foundation had been organized not on the basis
of purpose, like the operating agencies, not even on the basis of
the applied fields of science or development engineering, but on
the basis of the scientific disciplines, in order to be prepared to
deal with its clientele, the universities, and to handle its main
type of business, applications for the support of basic research
projects. This did not give the director of the Foundation the
kind of staff (in terms of either organization or personnel) that
would enable him to consider effectively the relation between
an operating agency's basic research program and the applied

research and development program that provides the payoff in terms of its end purposes.*

WHAT IS

Many more writers and participants in the events that shaped the legislation and then the growth of the National Science Foundation could be quoted to reveal the divergences of point of view that led, first, to the establishment of a science agency with both policy-making and research-support responsibilities and, second, to the apparent atrophy of the policy-making function.

As noted at the beginning of the chapter, the fundamental issues involved are open to many questions beyond the scope of this book. Suffice it to say that the Foundation today, after the changes produced by the Reorganization Act of 1962, the NSF retains little of its original policy-making function. It retains in full the broad research-support function, which serves as the base of its many far-reaching programs.

This diminution in function has produced some changes in administrative organization as the structure of the National Science Foundation has grown ever more complicated. That complex organization, aptly described by Price as having been set up "on the basis of the scientific disciplines . . . to deal with its clientele . . . and to handle . . . applications for the support of basic research projects" is the subject of the next chapter.

* Don K. Price, *The Scientific Estate* (Cambridge, Mass.: The Belknap Press of Harvard University Press, 1965), pp. 239–40. Copyright 1965 by the President and Fellows of Harvard College.

III

Present Administrative
Organization and Practices

The first section of the National Science Foundation Act describes the Foundation as an "independent agency," and later sections define in some detail the responsibilities of the National Science Board, the director of the NSF, and the various committees to be established by the board, the several divisions, the special advisory committees, councils, and commissions, employment of personnel, and the Science Information Service and Council. Since 1950, these sections have served as the authority for the organization of the Foundation and for its expansion as its program duties have increased.

The original organization of the Foundation, as described in its first annual report for 1950–51, was rather simple. Alan T. Waterman, former chief scientist of the Office of Naval Research, had been appointed director on April 6, 1950, and had promptly established a plan of organization based on the provisions of the law. The National Science Board, consisting of twenty-four members and the director, had been appointed on November 2, 1950. President Truman called its first meeting on December 12, 1950, at which time James B. Conant, president of Harvard University, was elected chairman. The board also appointed an executive committee of nine members under Detlev W. Bronk, president of Johns Hopkins University.

In the first organization there were four divisions (medical research, mathematical, physical and engineering sciences, biological sciences, and scientific personnel and education), each headed by an assistant director. The director's staff included a general counsel and an assistant director for administration, who had charge of the offices for scientific information, finance, and administration. The National Science Board had an executive secretary. The average number of employees for the part of the year 1950–51 during which the Foundation was in operation was only five, but in 1952 there was an average of sixty-four. By contrast, there have been more than nine hundred employees in recent years.

The organization of the Foundation is now far more complex than it was in the beginning, as the chart shows. But even this chart, which includes the principal divisions and the programs over which each division has jurisdiction, does not show the numerous part-time advisory committees, councils, commissions, and panels, which in recent years have numbered forty or more.

David Allison wrote in *International Science and Technology* (April, 1966) that:

. . . "the Foundation" is not Director Leland Haworth, nor the 300 professional people—most of them people with scientific backgrounds—who make up his staff. Practically speaking, the Foundation is Haworth, his staff, *plus* the 24 members of the National Science Board, *plus* some 39 advisory panels, divisional committees, councils, advisory committees, and so on, which are made up of several hundred scientists and engineers who represent various technical fields and who come to the Foundation periodically to advise on new programs and to evaluate the proposals that have been submitted by *other* scientists and engineers.

Thus, in reality, power is greatly diffused. You may wonder how *anything* can be accomplished in an organization so burdened with layers of authority.*

As an "independent agency" the National Science Foundation is to be distinguished from a "department" or a "regulatory agency" of the federal executive branch. (There have been movements to establish a department of science, similar

* Reprinted with permission from *Science and Technology*. Copyright 1966 by International Communications, Inc.

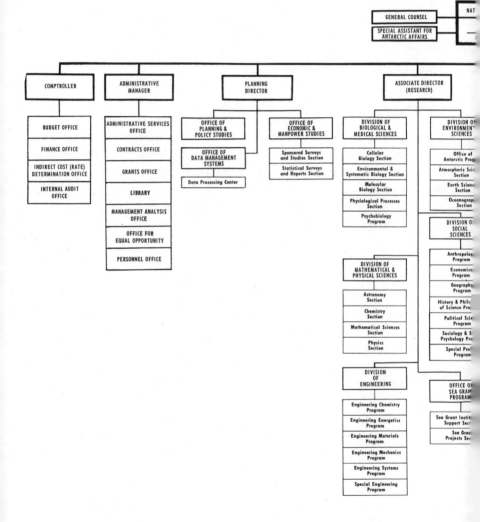

NAT

GENERAL COUNSEL

SPECIAL ASSISTANT FOR
ANTARCTIC AFFAIRS

COMPTROLLER

BUDGET OFFICE

FINANCE OFFICE

INDIRECT COST (RATE)
DETERMINATION OFFICE

INTERNAL AUDIT
OFFICE

**ADMINISTRATIVE
MANAGER**

ADMINISTRATIVE SERVICES
OFFICE

CONTRACTS OFFICE

GRANTS OFFICE

LIBRARY

MANAGEMENT ANALYSIS
OFFICE

OFFICE FOR
EQUAL OPPORTUNITY

PERSONNEL OFFICE

**PLANNING
DIRECTOR**

OFFICE OF
PLANNING &
POLICY STUDIES

OFFICE OF
DATA MANAGEMENT
SYSTEMS

Data Processing Center

OFFICE OF
ECONOMIC &
MANPOWER STUDIES

Sponsored Surveys
and Studies Section

Statistical Surveys
and Reports Section

**ASSOCIATE DIRECTOR
(RESEARCH)**

DIVISION OF
BIOLOGICAL &
MEDICAL SCIENCES

Cellular
Biology Section

Environmental &
Systematic Biology Section

Molecular
Biology Section

Physiological Processes
Section

Psychobiology
Program

DIVISION OF
MATHEMATICAL &
PHYSICAL SCIENCES

Astronomy
Section

Chemistry
Section

Mathematical Sciences
Section

Physics
Section

DIVISION
OF
ENGINEERING

Engineering Chemistry
Program

Engineering Energetics
Program

Engineering Materials
Program

Engineering Mechanics
Program

Engineering Systems
Program

Special Engineering
Program

DIVISION OF
ENVIRONMENT
SCIENCES

Office of
Antarctic Prog

Atmospheric Scie
Section

Earth Scienc
Section

Oceanograp
Section

DIVISION O
SOCIAL
SCIENCES

Anthropolo
Program

Economics
Program

Geography
Program

History & Phil
of Science Pro

Political Scie
Program

Sociology & S
Psychology Pr

Special Prol
Program

OFFICE O
SEA GRAN
PROGRAM

Sea Grant Instit
Support Sec

Sea Gra
Projects Se

July 1, 1968

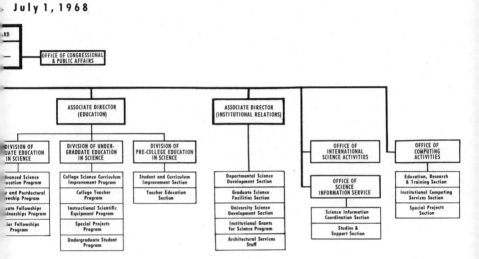

RD

OFFICE OF CONGRESSIONAL
& PUBLIC AFFAIRS

ASSOCIATE DIRECTOR
(EDUCATION)

ASSOCIATE DIRECTOR
(INSTITUTIONAL RELATIONS)

DIVISION OF
UATE EDUCATION
IN SCIENCE

DIVISION OF UNDER-
GRADUATE EDUCATION
IN SCIENCE

DIVISION OF
PRE-COLLEGE EDUCATION
IN SCIENCE

OFFICE OF
INTERNATIONAL
SCIENCE ACTIVITIES

OFFICE OF
COMPUTING
ACTIVITIES

dvanced Science
ucation Program

College Science Curriculum
Improvement Program

Student and Curriculum
Improvement Section

Departmental Science
Development Section

OFFICE OF
SCIENCE
INFORMATION SERVICE

Education, Research
& Training Section

r and Postdoctoral
wship Program

College Teacher
Program

Teacher Education
Section

Graduate Science
Facilities Section

Institutional Computing
Services Section

uate Fellowships
ineeships Program

Instructional Scientific
Equipment Program

University Science
Development Section

Science Information
Coordination Section

Special Projects
Section

ior Fellowships
Program

Special Projects
Program

Institutional Grants
for Science Program

Studies &
Support Section

Undergraduate Student
Program

Architectural Services
Staff

to other major departments, which would include the National Science Foundation as one of the constituent parts. These movements, however, have not been successful.) The Foundation is unlike the Office of Science and Technology, the National Aeronautics and Space Council, and the Federal Council for Science and Technology, all located in the Executive Office as advisory agencies with responsibility to the President only. The Foundation is not, however, like certain of the independent agencies having regulatory powers over different private enterprise sectors of the national economy— for example, the Interstate Commerce Commission. The National Science Foundation is included in a class of agencies possessing no important regulatory powers. Some of them are headed by boards or commissions (for example, the Atomic Energy Commission) but Congress devised a different pattern for the NSF.

If the organization and powers of these different types of agencies are examined carefully, it is difficult to explain their "independence." In the case of the Foundation, Congress passed the original law with later amendments, which constitutes the basis for its organization and powers; Congress annually appropriates its funds; and Congress reviews its operations. The President appoints the director, by and with the advice and consent of the Senate, and he can remove him. The National Science Board members are appointed by and with the advice and consent of the Senate; there is no legal provision for their removal. The Foundation can accurately be described as "independent" of the fourteen departments, but it is subject to the powers of the Congress and the President just as are all the other departments and agencies of the executive branch of the government.

The simple statement that the Foundation shall consist of the director and the board is considerably complicated by later provisions of the act, which specify the duties of each. A "two-headed" chief executive is unusual—and potentially a cause of difficulty. Clearly, Congress intended that the director and the board should be equals, and important powers were assigned to each in the act. Dael Wolfle, in an article in *Science* (August 23, 1957), described this structure as representing "a compromise between two opposed ideas of appropriate organization that were debated all through the legislative history of the National Science Foundation Act." At that time, the arrangement seemed to be working satisfactorily, and Wolfle, recapitulating its history, wrote:

> One group of supporters thought the foundation should be headed by a Presidentially appointed board of 48 (later reduced to 24) distinguished representatives of the fields of science, education, and public affairs. This board was to be empowered to select the director of the foundation. The director, under this arrangement, would have been responsible to the board rather than to the President. Advocates of this structure hoped that a large board would insure wide representation of the views of scientific leaders, expected that the responsibility of membership would make appointment attractive to men of high competence, and believed that this administrative structure would guarantee against the appointment of the foundation's director on political grounds.
>
> In contrast, other supporters of a science foundation—including, apparently, a majority of scientists—thought the director should be appointed by, and should be directly responsible to, the President. To advise the director and his staff, advocates of this administrative structure recommended the appointment of an advisory board, smaller in size than the supervisory board called for by adherents of the other school of thought. Advocates of this structure pointed out that such an arrangement was in better agreement with usual ideas of good governmental administration and argued that a large board would so diffuse responsibility that no one could be held responsible for the success or failure of the organization.
>
> This issue was more vigorously debated than any other aspect of the foundation idea. Yet once the bill became law, the argument quickly died. It is impossible to say how well an alternative type of organization would have worked. . . . The absence of any attempt to change the administrative structure is a testimonial to both the board and the director, for good cooperation has been essential and has apparently been achieved.

Ten years later, in 1967, a different judgment was passed on the dual executive that heads the Foundation. It is correct to say that throughout this period the director and the board had worked well together, but by 1967 there was no longer any lack of attempts to change the Foundation's administrative structure. By law, by reorganization plan, and by executive order, there had been several changes, but none of them was basic. A powerful movement for fundamental revision came between 1965 and 1967, however, and to date the problems raised have not been resolved. This recent movement is described in Chapter XII.

The National Science Foundation Act provided that the Foundation would be composed of a national science board and a director, but there is some question about which should be described first. The act contains a section on the board followed by one on the director. However, following sections dealing with the many different powers, duties, and functions specify the Foundation as a whole or the director or the board or some combination of the director and the board as the performing agency. One result is that describing the board and the director separately is fairly simple so far as their organization on paper is concerned but almost impossible if a description of their functional responsibility is attempted.

The National Science Board

The twenty-five members of the National Science Board, in the words of the act of 1950:

(1) shall be eminent in the fields of the basic sciences, medical science, engineering, agriculture, education, or public affairs; (2) shall be selected solely on the basis of established records of distinguished service; and (3) shall be so selected as to provide representation of the views of scientific leaders in all areas of the Nation. The President is requested, in the making of nominations of persons for appointment as members, to give due consideration to any recommendations for nomination which may be submitted to him by the National Academy of Sciences, the Association of Land Grant Colleges and Universi-

ties, the National Association of State Universities, the Association of American Colleges, or by other scientific or educational organizations.

The term of office for these nominees appointed by the President, with the advice and consent of the Senate and of the NSF director, is six years, with the terms of one-third of the members expiring every two years. Reappointment for a second term is permitted, but the member is not eligible for reappointment for two years after the end of his second term. Vacancies are filled for the remainder of the term of the predecessor.

The board meets annually in May and also meets whenever the chairman calls for it or whenever one-third of the members so request in writing. A majority of voting members constitutes a quorum. Notice by mail of a meeting is required. Every two years, the board elects a chairman and a vice chairman, and the board elects a member to fill a vacancy in either office.

Members of the board are paid $50 for each day in which they are engaged in the business of the Foundation, and they receive travel expenses as provided by law. In recent years, they have met about nine times a year. Their service is exempt from conflict-of-interest legal restrictions except with respect to any matter directly involving the Foundation.

The board is authorized to appoint from among its members an executive committee, to which it may assign such of its powers and duties (except that of establishing Foundation policies) as it deems appropriate. It also appoints other committees for survey and advisory functions. The executive committee consists of the director and not less than five nor more than nine members elected by the board. At present, there are five members—the director of the Foundation as chairman, the chairman and the vice chairman of the board, and two other board members. The term of office of these members is two years, and after three terms a member is ineligible for reappointment for two years. The executive committee makes an annual report to the board, and other reports if necessary, summarizing its activities and making appropriate recommendations. If there are minority views and recommendations they are included in the report. These reports are not published.

The National Science Foundation is required to make an annual report to the President for submission to Congress. In practice, this report is made by the director, but the law provides that, if there are minority views and recommendations of members of the board, they must be included. In the early years of the Foundation's existence, annual reports included statements by board chairmen. They are not found in reports of recent years.

From 1945, five years before Congress created the Foundation, to the present time there has been continuing discussion of the proper roles of the board and the director, and an entire book could be written on that one aspect of the Foundation. It is easy to say that the board "makes policy" for the NSF and the director executes it. But two complicating factors are written into the act itself—(1) the board, which determines policy, includes the director as a member and as chairman of the executive committee of the board, thus placing him in an important role in policy formulation; and (2) there are many provisions in the law requiring the approval of the board for actions of the director, which he must have to administer programs. Thus, the National Science Board as the agency determining NSF policy has a rather mixed role. It shares policy, operational, and advisory functions (duties) with the director in a relationship that is still evolving. Although originally, the board was intended to be a group of eminent scientists who made the grants, which the director and his staff would administer, neither the board nor the director has undivided responsibility. Indeed, the board has more duties—both policy-making and administrative—than it was planned to have.

In the absence of published reports by the National Science Board and its executive committee, it is impossible to describe with precision exactly what these two bodies do, but directors of the Foundation and chairmen and members of the board have made many statements indicating their harmonious working relationships.

THE DIRECTOR OF THE NATIONAL SCIENCE FOUNDATION

The chief executive officer of the Foundation, as provided in the National Science Foundation Act, is the director. He is appointed by the President, by and with the consent of the Senate. In the Senate, the Labor and Public Welfare Committee has jurisdiction over all legislative matters concerning the Foundation, and the name of the President's nominee is sent to it for consideration before the Senate votes on confirmation. The Foundation to date has had two directors—both of them distinguished scientists with outstanding records in the federal government's scientific programs.

In 1951, President Harry S Truman named Alan T. Waterman director. He served until his retirement in 1963. After an early career as a university teacher, Waterman spent two years during World War I with the science and research division of the Army Signal Corps, and during World War II he held different positions in the Office of Scientific Research and Development. In 1946, he became deputy chief and chief scientist of the newly established Office of Naval Research, and he went directly from the ONR to the Foundation. Waterman is credited with following the precepts of the Bush report, *Science—The Endless Frontier,* and, in collaboration with the National Science Board, of having established the basic philosophy still guiding the Foundation in its programs in support of basic research. After he retired, he was active in many different advisory and administrative activities—for example, as special consultant to the president of the National Academy of Sciences before his death in 1967.

After Waterman's retirement, President John F. Kennedy nominated Leland J. Haworth director. Before World War II, Haworth was a university teacher, and from 1941 to 1946 he worked on defense projects at the MIT Radiation Laboratory. In 1948, he was appointed director of the Brookhaven

National Laboratory; while holding this position he became president of Associated Universities, Inc., and a member of the board of directors of the Oak Ridge Institute for Nuclear Studies. He became a member of the Atomic Energy Commission in 1961. Like Waterman, Haworth has served on a large number of important special scientific committees and project groups.

The National Science Foundation Act has many provisions relating to the office of director. It provides that the National Science Board may make recommendations to the President with respect to appointment of the director, and that he shall not be appointed until the board has had the opportunity to make recommendations. The director has a term of office of six years unless removed by the President, and he is a member of the board with the right to vote. The law says:

> . . . the Director shall, in accordance with policies established by the Board, exercise the powers granted by sections 1869 [scholarships and graduate fellowships] and 1870 [general authority of the Foundation] of this title, together with such other powers and duties as may be delegated to him by the Board; but no final action shall be taken by the Director in the exercise of any power granted by section 1869 or 1870 (c) [award of contracts for certain scientific activities undertaken at the request of the Secretary of Defense] of this title unless in each instance the Board has reviewed and approved the action proposed to be taken, or such action is taken pursuant to the terms of a delegation of authority from the Board or the Executive Committee to the Director.

This general and rather complicated grant of power does not give any specific idea of the director's important duties. They are also specified by law, however. In brief, he is the general executive officer in charge of managing all the programs of the Foundation (which are described in chapters V through X); he must prepare for and attend the meetings of the National Science Board and its executive committee because he is a voting member of each body and chairman of the committee; he is the principal formal contact of the Foundation with the members and the committees of the Congress, which involves furnishing information and, particularly, appearing as a witness; and he is a member of several additional organizations, including the Federal Council for Science and Technology, the Defense Science Board, and the President's Committee on Manpower. Although he is not a member of the Office of Science and Technology in the Executive Office of the President, he works in close contact with it, as he also does with the National Academy of Sciences and other bodies.

As the chief executive officer of an agency with nearly a thousand staff members, an annual budget of nearly $500 million, and a complex collection of active programs, the director probably could be kept busy without his additional—but extremely important—duties as a member of several different policy-making groups, and as the Foundation's principal contact with Congress. He is permitted to appoint, with the approval of the board, a deputy director who performs such duties as he, with the approval of the board, may prescribe. This official becomes acting head of the Foundation if the director is absent or disabled, or in the event of a vacancy in the office of director. In accordance with policies established by the board, the director also makes appointments of certain members of the staff, including members of divisional committees and special commissions, and certain technical and professional personnel who are hired without regard to the civil service laws under which other personnel serve.

The director's salary (under an act of 1967) is $29,500 per year, and his deputy receives $26,000.

Each year, the Foundation makes a report to the President, who transfers it to Congress. The director's statements in these reports, and his testimony before the appropriations committees and other committees of the Congress, are excellent sources of information about his policies.

Advisory Committees, Councils, and Commissions

The different types of advisory bodies are extremely important elements in the Foundation's structure. Through their members, the Foundation is in close and constant contact with representatives of all the different fields of science, in all parts of the country. Those who have feared that federal aid to science would result in excessive decision and control by the federal government are reassured by procedures that insure that leaders of the scientific community are playing an active part in deciding the course to be taken by scientific research and science education.

A quotation from the Foreword in the Foundation's annual report for 1952 stated the policy of the Foundation as it has existed from its beginning:

> An ever-present danger inherent in any governmental organization for promotion of basic science lies in its propensity to exercise the kind and degree of control which is appropriate to research and development more closely related to immediate practical ends. The chief safeguard against this danger, outside the integrity and understanding of the Director and members of the Board, is the extensive, active cooperation of scientists who are not part of the regular staff of the Foundation. For wise judgment of the merits of specific research proposals the Foundation depends upon those most competent and respected in their various fields. Such advice is a personal thing, relating not only to subject matter, but to character, scientific competence, and integrity of those to whom support is to be given.

> The collaboration of scientists is also indispensable in the discharge of the functions of the Foundation in evaluating scientific progress and scientific needs. The term "evaluation" suggests to many the idea of direction or control—factors thought to be inimical to effective basic scientific research. It has been widely held that creative and imaginative research in science as in certain other fields is necessarily individualistic and unorganizable except for informal or more or less spontaneous collaboration. In large degree this may always be true, but it may well be that we have reached the stage of social development where deliberate collaboration of specialists and concerted development of ideas is possible and necessary. . . . In any event the act requires the Foundation to evaluate scientific progress and to locate fields that need scientific development, and it is difficult to see how the Foundation could carry out its functions otherwise.

. . . Clearly, in embarking upon the problem of evaluation—an undertaking of great delicacy and intricacy in which our society now must pioneer—the collaboration of the scientific community is indispensable.

The original act of 1950 established a committee for each division of the Foundation, specifying the number of members, their terms of office, a chairman, rules, and their duty to make recommendations to, and to advise and consult with the director and the board. Members of each committee were appointed by the board. As time went on, the number of divisions increased, there were more interrelationships among their activities, and it became apparent that a more flexible arrangement was needed. This was provided in Reorganization Plan No. 5 of 1965, which abolished the divisional committees provided in the original act.

Since that change, the director, under his general authority to appoint consultants, has established a system of functional "advisory committees." He appoints the members in consultation with the board. Each advisory committee has as its principal concern the activities of a division or a group of divisions, but each has been requested to consider all activities bearing on its field of interest throughout the Foundation, and to maintain awareness of the activities of all other committees. Each committee has been asked to prepare a written annual report to the director, and each committee chairman makes an oral presentation before the board each year.

In the Foundation's annual report for 1966, there was a listing of members of the following advisory committees: biological and medical sciences, engineering, institutional relations, mathematical and physical sciences, science education, and social sciences.

The act of 1950 also provided for establishment of special commissions to make comprehensive surveys of research in particular fields and to formulate for the Foundation over-all research programs in these fields. Thus, the special Commission for Rubber Research was set up and terminated in 1956, and the Special Commission on Weather Modification was in existence in 1964 and 1965. Each commission consists of eleven members appointed by the board, six of whom shall be eminent scientists and five nonscientists.

Special advisory panels are created to provide short-term or intermittent advisory service. They are appointed by the director. Many university faculty and industrial research personnel serve on these panels, usually for a term of two years, and several hundred consultants are available for such service.

In the 1966 annual report of the Foundation, advisory panels were listed for Antarctic programs, anthropology, astronomy, atmospheric sciences, biological facilities and special programs, chemistry, developmental biology, earth sciences, economics, economic and manpower studies, environmental biology, genetic biology, history and philosophy of science, manpower and education studies programs, mathematical sciences, metabolic biology, molecular biology, oceanographic facilities, physics, psychobiology, radio telescopes, regulatory biology, science development, sociology and social psychology, systematic biology, computing facilities, and weather modification.

The Science Information Council

Section 1877 of the National Science Foundation Act contains provision for the Science Information Council as a part of the Science Information Service, established in the Foundation in 1958. Chapter VIII of this book describes the council in some detail. Its duty is to advise, consult with, and make recommendations to the head of the Science Information Service. Reorganization Plan No. 5 of 1965, which abolished the divisional committees established in the original National Science Foundation Act, did not abolish the Science Information Council.

The National Council on Marine Resources and Development

The National Sea Grant College and Program Act of 1966 contains a section referring to the National Council on Marine

Resources and Development, established under a closely related law, the Marine Resources and Development Act of 1966. This council is located in the Executive Office of the President, and the director of the National Science Foundation is one of its nine members. The Foundation is given the administration of the National Sea Grant College and Program Act. As the President may request, the National Council is directed to advise the Foundation in the administration of this program, to provide policy guidance and make recommendations with respect to contracts or grants, and to report its actions annually to the Speaker of the House of Representatives, the Committee on Merchant Marine and Fisheries of the House of Representatives, the President of the Senate, and the Senate Committee on Labor and Public Welfare.

PERSONNEL

In fiscal year 1966, the National Science Foundation had sixty-two special positions at rates equal to or in excess of $23,013. These were the director, $28,500; the deputy director, $26,000; three associate directors at $25,382 each; the administrative manager, $25,382; the comptroller, $25,382; the general counsel, $25,382; the congressional liaison officer, $25,382; and a project director (Mohole), $25,382. Fifty-two others had salaries ranging from $19,619 to $25,040. In addition, there were more than nine hundred employees in civil service general schedule grades and grades established by NSF equivalent to schedule grades. These ranged from 117 GS-15's at $17,550 to $23,013, to 15 GS-2's at $3,925 to $5,122.

Table 1* was presented by the Foundation during the appropriation hearings for fiscal year 1968.

ADMINISTRATIVE SECURITY

Section 1874 of the National Science Foundation Act contains the security provisions under which the Foundation op-

---

* This table and all subsequent tables are based on NSF, Bureau of the Budget, congressional-committee, and other official government reports.

TABLE 1
Personnel Summary, 1968

National Science Foundation	1966 Actual	1967 Estimate	1968 Estimate
Total permanent positions	985	1,000	1,025
Full-time equivalents of other positions	40	40	43
Average number of all employees	947	983	992
Average GS grade	8.8	9.0	9.2
Average GS salary	$9,667	$10,120	$10,449
Average salary of ungraded positions	$20,450	$21,290	$21,715
*Library of Congress**			
Total permanent positions	26	—	—
Average number of all employees	23	—	—
Average GS grade	5.8	—	—
Average GS salary	$6,542	—	—

* National Referral Center for Science and related activities.

erates. They have a significant effect on administration. Paragraph (a) establishes conditions under which the NSF cooperates with the Atomic Energy Commission. The commission's regulations concerning dissemination of restricted data and security clearance for individuals having access to it control the Foundation in any cases where its support of an activity involves research in nuclear energy.

Paragraph (b) deals with research in the area of national defense: (1) if funds are transferred to the Foundation by the Department of Defense (as provided in section 1873[h]), the Secretary of Defense establishes necessary security safeguards; (2) in other research activities concerning national defense, supported by NSF funds, the Foundation establishes the security safeguards; and (3) other agencies of government exercising investigatory functions are authorized to assist the Foundation in maintaining its security safeguards.

Paragraph (c) provides that all Foundation employees who have access to information or property to which restrictions have been imposed under paragraphs (a) and (b), must have been investigated by the Civil Service Commission. The Foundation determines on the basis of this report whether the employment of a person will "endanger the common defense and security."

Paragraphs (a), (b), and (c) have not caused particular objections, but paragraph (d) has been, at times, extremely controversial. As a result, the original provisions of this paragraph, entitled "Oath and statement prerequisite to acceptance of scholarship or fellowship; ineligibility of Communist organization members; penalties" were amended in 1962. Today, the oath to which a person must subscribe if he accepts appointment to a scholarship or fellowship is, "I do solemnly swear (or affirm) that I bear true faith and allegiance to the United States of America and will support and defend the Constitution and laws of the United States against all its enemies, foreign and domestic."

An individual who accepts a scholarship or fellowship must furnish to the Foundation a statement containing the details of any crimes of which he has been convicted and any criminal charges that are pending.

The idea of loyalty as a consideration in federal support of nonclassified basic scientific research originated in efforts to protect national security during and after World War II. The necessity for protecting the security of the United States was balanced against the need for research and dissemination of scientific information. In 1945, Vannevar Bush, who had had experience with this problem during wartime, and who was well aware of the views of the scientific community, expressed his belief in *Science—the Endless Frontier* that, except to the extent that military security dictated otherwise, the knowledge and information gained during the war should be "spread on the record for the benefit of the general public." There was no reason to doubt that scientists of other countries would in time rediscover everything the United States was holding in secrecy, he felt, and continued:

A broad dissemination of scientific information upon which further advances can readily be made furnishes a sounder foundation for our national security than a policy of restriction which would impede our own progress although imposed in the hope that possible enemies would not catch up with us.

Our ability to overcome possible future enemies depends upon scientific advances which will proceed more rapidly with diffusion of knowledge than under a policy of continued restriction of knowledge now in our possession.

He proposed a plan to coordinate the release of scientific information by the different departments and agencies and recommended immediate adoption of measures to facilitate publication of the materials released from security control. In practice, however, more problems arose than Bush had anticipated in his 1945 report. The Foundation ran into difficulties, as evidenced by inclusion in its annual reports of the mid-1950's of sections on loyalty and security in relation to grants for unclassified research. See particularly the reports for 1954, 1955, and 1956.

The position of the Foundation in this area has always been clear, but the 1955 annual report set forth at some length the practices established in World War II and the general administrative principles governing the Foundation's then current practices. Saying that "when national security is not involved, inquiry into the political thoughts and beliefs of individuals has traditionally been contrary to American principles," the statement continues:

Bearing in mind the considerations mentioned above, the policy of the National Science Foundation in processing proposals for grants in support of unclassified research, not involving considerations of security, is to assure that in appraising the merit of a proposal for unclassified research submitted by or on behalf of a scientist, his experience, competence, and integrity are always taken carefully into account by scientists having a working knowledge of his qualifications. However, the Foundation does not knowingly give nor continue a grant in support of research for one who is:

1. An avowed Communist or anyone established as being a Communist by a judicial proceeding, or by an unappealed determination by the Attorney General or the Subversive Activities

Control Board pursuant to the Subversive Activities Control Act of 1950, or anyone who avowedly advocates change in the U.S. Government by other than constitutional means, or,

2. An individual who has been convicted of sabotage, espionage, sedition, subversive activity under the Smith Act, or a similar crime involving the nation's security.*

The Foundation . . . will not knowingly support anyone who is, by admission or conviction, disloyal to this country. In the interest of science, however, it will not pass judgment on the loyalty of an individual on the basis of unsupported charges but will rely upon the judgment of those who best know the individual and his qualifications. This position of the Foundation has been endorsed by the American Association for the Advancement of Science in a resolution passed at its annual meeting in Berkeley last winter. We believe it to be in the best interests of the nation.

In the 1956 annual report, the Foundation repeated much of the 1955 statement and added the text of recommendations made by the Committee on Loyalty in Relation to Government Support of Unclassified Research, appointed by the president of the National Academy of Sciences. These recommendations were essentially like the policies stated by the Foundation, and the departments and agencies of the federal government were instructed by the White House to follow practices consistent with them.

* Because the law requiring registration of Communist organizations with the Subversive Activities Control Board has become practically unenforceable, there is question about the effectiveness of these two provisions.

IV

The Foundation's Finances

The financing of science is one of today's major problems. To people administering research and development programs in government and outside it, it is the major problem. More programs, more scientists, increased costs, greater expectations on the part of the public as to the benefits to be derived—all these factors are making it inevitable that more funds from all sources must be forthcoming. In addition, the competing claims of other programs—particularly those created by the conflict in Vietnam and the new and expanded welfare programs—make it necessary to clarify and intensify the claims supporting expenditures for research. To some individuals, science's priority is rather far down the list. They say that maybe we can have guns and butter, but not guns and *paté de foie gras*. To them, the financing of research and development seems something that can be deferred or at least merely held at present levels until better days have come.

This chapter considers different aspects of the subject of finances—a matter that needs to be understood before NSF programs and expenditures for programs can be dealt with. It covers the source of the Foundation's authority to expend funds, its annual appropriations, and its expenditures, including administrative costs; it compares Foundation support with that of the research programs of other federal agencies and all the various sources of support of research; and it discusses the general subject of the adequacy of federal support of research.

FINANCIAL AUTHORITY OF THE FOUNDATION

Each agency of the federal government receives the funds to carry out its functions through an act of Congress. In some cases—for example, the National Aeronautics and Space Administration—Congress first passes an act authorizing expenditures for the coming fiscal year and then passes an act appropriating a specific amount of money. In the case of the NSF, no annual authorization is necessary. The National Science Foundation Act (section 1875) provides that "to enable the Foundation to carry out its powers and duties, there is authorized to be appropriated to the Foundation, out of any money in the Treasury not otherwise appropriated, such sums as may be necessary. . . ." These sums will "remain available for obligation, for expenditure, or for obligation and expenditure, for such period or periods as may be specified in the acts making such appropriations."

Additionally, in 1958, the Science Information Service was established as part of the National Science Foundation, and the legislation contained a section authorizing annual appropriation of necessary funds. In 1966, the National Sea Grant College and Program Act contained authorization for the appropriation for fiscal year 1967 of an amount not exceeding $5 million, for 1968 not exceeding $15 million, and for later years "only such sums as Congress may hereafter specifically authorize by law." Each year, Congress enacts legislation appropriating funds under this authorization.

ANNUAL APPROPRIATIONS

In the original act establishing the Foundation, Congress included authorization of an appropriation not to exceed $500,000 for fiscal year 1951, and not to exceed $15 million for each fiscal year thereafter. In 1953, this provision was amended to read "such sums as may be necessary to carry out the provisions of this act." In fact, appropriation of more than $15 million was not made until fiscal year 1956.

Congress may provide that an appropriation will remain available for such period as it provides in each annual appropriation act. Many federal departments and agencies lose all unexpended and unobligated funds at the end of each year. From the beginning, the Foundation has usually had "no-year" funds—that is, their funds remain available until expended, rather than lapsing to the Treasury at the end of the fiscal year. "No-year" funds make it possible to plan programs on a long-range basis—a necessity for the Foundation in view of the kind of programs it supports. During recent fiscal years, the funds expended had been appropriated in several different acts of preceding years.

Any department or agency of the federal government that has funds available for scientific or technical research, or provision of facilities for such research, may transfer funds to the Foundation to be expended for the purposes for which the funds were appropriated. In 1966, the Foundation received funds totaling $2,412,000 under special foreign currency programs, from funds appropriated to the President and to the departments of Agriculture, of Health, Education, and Welfare, and the Interior.

The Foundation not only receives funds from other agencies, but it also transfers funds to various agencies to carry out assigned functions. In 1964, 1965, and 1966, the Foundation was forbidden to transfer funds in this manner without the approval of the Bureau of the Budget, but Congress expressed the view that, if other agencies needed funds, the requests should be included in their respective budgets so that Congress could act on them directly. Objections to this process led Congress to omit the prohibition in the appropriation acts for 1967 and 1968. In 1965, the NSF transferred $166,521 to other agencies, and in 1966 it transferred $175,000 to the Library of Congress for such purposes as abstracting and indexing services, various publications, and support of the National Referral Center for Science and Technology.

The Foundation is authorized to receive and use funds donated to it. Such funds must be available without restriction except that they be used to carry out the purposes of the act. The Department of the Treasury carries these funds under a special trust account. During its first fiscal year, the Foundation received a donation of $512 from the Committee Supporting the Bush Report. The gifts in any one year have been relatively small, ranging from $2,333 in 1962 to $618 in 1966, as have expenditures from the trust fund.

The following appropriations (in thousands of dollars) have been made to the Foundation in the fiscal years noted:

1951	$ 225
1952	3,500
1953	4,750
1954	8,000
1955	12,250
1956	16,000
1957	40,000
1958	40,000
1959	130,000
1960	152,773
1961	175,800
1962	263,250
1963	322,500
1964	353,200
1965	420,400
1966	479,999
1967	479,999
1968	495,000

In addition to appropriations for the Foundation, separate appropriations for the International Geophysical Year were made in five instances and for synthetic rubber research and development in one instance. In 1958 and 1959, funds were transferred to the Foundation in the appropriation acts for the Atomic Energy Commission.

The actual provisions of the appropriation acts during the life of the Foundation have varied considerably. A review of them indicates strikingly what a powerful control Congress exercises over the conduct of the Foundation's affairs through the annual appropriations.

Without naming each specific provision, they can be summarized to indicate the nature of these controls. For example, in the early years, the Foundation was allowed to purchase one motor vehicle; later, it could also hire vehicles; from 1953 through 1962, it could only hire, not purchase; and since 1963, the right to hire has continued, and there have been new provisions relating to purchase of motor vehicles and the operation and maintenance of aircraft and purchase of flight services for research purposes.

Employment and payment of experts and consultants were authorized, and in 1968 the Foundation's exercise of this power was placed under the general law controlling all federal departments and agencies in such kinds of employment.

Specified amounts for travel expenses were allowed before 1960, but since that time there has been no mention of this item.

Every year there is authorization for funds for awards of graduate fellowships but no specific amounts are named.

Provision is included for reimbursement to General Services Administration for security guard service.

In 1957 and 1958, funds were provided for supplementary training of high school teachers, and an increased amount was allowed in 1959. From 1960 through fiscal 1968, funds were provided for supplementary training of secondary school teachers.

The Foundation was permitted, in 1961–67, to purchase specified amounts of foreign currencies for various scientific and technological functions that it conducts outside the United States, but the 1968 appropriation act did not include this provision.

The new program under the National Sea Grant College and Program Act of 1966 became operative in fiscal year 1967. The law making supplemental appropriations for that year authorized the Foundation to expend $1 million to finance the new program, using funds already appropriated for its general purposes.

In the acts for 1964, 1965, and 1966 it was provided that "no part of the foregoing appropriation may be transferred to any other agency of government for research without the approval of the Bureau of the Budget." This provision was not included in the acts for 1967 and 1968.

A few additional minor provisions have been included in some years.

NSF Expenditures for Scientific Research and Development

The amounts of money the National Science Foundation requests for carrying out its program and the amounts it is actually permitted to expend are never the same, and usually the request is considerably more than the appropriation. In the first eighteen years of its career, the Foundation never received an appropriation as large as its budget request. (The budget requests of other departments and agencies nearly always suffer the same fate.) In the first four years, Congress did not appropriate anywhere near the amounts requested. In 1957, by contrast, the request and the appropriation were only a little more than $1 million apart. In 1966, 1967, and 1968, the Foundation tried to break the half-billion dollar barrier, but Congress did not cooperate. For fiscal year 1968, however, the appropriation came within $5 million of the half-billion mark.

In its annual reports, the Foundation always includes an itemized statement of its obligations, broken down by various program activities. The details of the support of each activity are included in the chapters of this book describing programs.

Many people, particularly those in the colleges and universities, are concerned about the distribution of the Foundation's funds by academic disciplines. Information on this matter was included in the Foundation's 1966 report. A few high points may be noted. That year, biology received the largest amount of money ($79 million) and astronomy the least

($24 million). The money for the different disciplines had been used for seven different types of activity. Scientific research received $136 million and the amounts for science education, institutional support, information, international activities, planning and policy studies, and program development and management ranged down to a low of $900,000 for international science activities.

COMPARISON OF NSF FUNDS WITH THOSE OF OTHER AGENCIES

In 1952, the first full year of the Foundation's existence, NSF received an appropriation of about $3.5 million. Total federal obligations for research for that year are not available. But for *basic* research, the over-all federal amount was $71 million. Since the NSF expended funds chiefly for basic research, these two figures are roughly comparable. Five years later, the Foundation had $40 million to spend, federal obligations for basic research were $210 million, and total federal obligations for all research were $916 million. By 1965 (the most recent year for which comparable data of these three items are available) the Foundation had $420 million; federal obligations for basic research were an estimated $2.1 billion; and total federal obligations for research some $5 billion. The amount for the Foundation increased in thirteen years from $3.5 to $420 million; the amount for federal obligations for basic research went from $71 million to $2.1 billion; and federal obligations for all research ranged from $844 million in 1955 to over $5 billion in 1965.

Care must be exercised in comparing data on research and development funds, in order that one avoid comparing apples with oranges. To guard against this sort of error, data for three different purposes (research and development, research, and basic research) are combined in Table 2, which shows the position of the Foundation relative to total federal expenditures and relative to the four agencies with larger expenditures for these purposes. The Foundation was the only one of the five agencies that in 1966–68 expended all of its research

TABLE 2
Federal Research Expenditures, 1966–68
(in Billions of Dollars)

	Research and Development			Research			Basic Research		
	1966	1967*	1968*	1966	1967*	1968*	1966	1967*	1968*
Defense†	$6.7	$7.1	$7.7	$1.8	$1.8	$2.1	$0.3	$0.3	$0.3
NASA	5.9	5.6	5.3	1.3	1.4	1.5	0.6	0.7	0.9
AEC	1.4	1.4	1.6	0.4	0.4	0.4	0.3	0.3	0.3
HEW	0.9	1.1	1.2	0.8	1.0	1.1	0.3	0.4	0.4
NSF	0.2	0.3	0.3	0.2	0.2	0.2	0.2	0.2	0.2
Other	0.8	0.9	1.0	0.5	0.6	0.6	0.2	0.1	0.2
TOTAL‡	$16.0	$16.6	$17.1	$5.1	$5.3	$5.9	$1.8	$2.0	$2.3

* Estimated.
† Data for 1966 include military and civil functions; for 1967 and 1968, military functions only.
‡ Owing to rounding off, totals may not equal sums of numbers above them.

funds for basic research. This characteristic differentiates the Foundation from the other departments and agencies. The Department of Defense, the National Aeronautics and Space Administration, the Atomic Energy Commission, and the Department of Health, Education, and Welfare expend large amounts of their funds for development and other large amounts for applied research closely related to their major functions—what is called "mission-oriented" research. The Foundation spends very little on development. Practically all its money is spent on basic research. In fact, the support of basic research is the Foundation's mission, just as applied research relating to satellites is the mission of NASA. In 1966, the NSF spent less than 1.5 per cent of total federal expenditures for research and development, about 3.5 per cent of federal expenditures for research, and about 10 per cent of federal expenditures for basic research.

This fact may come as a surprise because there is a rather general impression that the Foundation has under its jurisdiction practically all basic research supported by the federal government. The contrary fact is stated without implied approval or disapproval. The Foundation undoubtedly would like to have a larger share of this function. However, the departments and agencies make a strong case for keeping large portions of basic research in fields close to their mission-oriented applied research and development. When the annual expenditures for these items have climbed into the billions, and when so many departments and agencies are responsible for them, it is perhaps humanly impossible to make a better distribution than presently exists. But the problem is continually under consideration in the executive branch and the Congress, and in the universities and the scientific community, and partial solutions are attempted, particularly through the annual appropriations process.

COMPARISON OF THE VARIOUS SOURCES OF SUPPORT FOR SCIENTIFIC RESEARCH

In comparing the expenditures for scientific research from different sources, the information is usually classified under the headings of federal government, industry, universities proper, and other nonprofit institutions. Since some of these spending agencies use not only their own funds but also money furnished by the other agencies, a somewhat complicated situation results.

Consideration of the various sources of support for scientific research is not easy because the term "support," unless it is carefully defined, may be misunderstood. "Support" can mean the source that furnished the funds, or it can mean the source that expended funds to pay for research. For example, the federal government, through grants and contracts with universities, uses the very large proportion of its funds for basic research, but the actual expenditure of these funds is made by the universities.

The rapid growth in the size of funds from four sources for research and development and for basic research is illustrated by Table 3, which shows that (1) funds for total research and development increased about 4 times while those for basic research increased over 7 times; (2) the federal government increased funds for research and development nearly 6 times, and funds for basic research about 9 times; (3) industry's rate of increase for research and development was about 3 times and for basic research, about 5 times; (4) the universities' funds for research and development increased 3 times and for basic research over 7 times; and, finally (5) nonprofit institutions increased their research and development funds about 2½ times and their basic research funds by a slightly higher rate. This shows that the federal government, in the first place, and the universities and colleges, in the second place, are the principal sources of increase in funds for all research and development, and particularly in funds for basic research.

The funds available to the National Science Foundation are

TABLE 3
Growth in Research Expenditures, 1953–65
(in Billions of Dollars)

	Research and Development		Basic Research	
	1953	1965	1953	1965
Federal government	$2.8	$13.1	$0.2	$1.9
Industry	2.2	6.6	0.1	0.5
Universities	0.2	0.6	0.07	0.5
Other nonprofit institutions	0.07	0.2	0.03	0.1
TOTAL*	$5.27	$20.5	$0.49	$2.9

* Owing to rounding off, totals may not equal sums of numbers above them.

intended almost entirely for basic research. They are expended both by the Foundation itself and to a large extent by colleges and universities. Currently, funds furnished by the Foundation are expended in the following sectors (figures are approximate):

Colleges and universities	$360 million
Other nonprofit organizations	60
Individuals	30
Industry	35
Other government agencies	10

The question of how much money should be spent for science has no answer—or rather it has too many answers. How much have we been spending? Is this the right amount? Is it properly distributed among the expending agencies (government, universities, private foundations, industry)? Is it properly distributed between basic research and applied research and development? Is it properly distributed between physical and natural and social sciences and the humanities? How does the National Science Foundation fare in this complex situation? Most of the questions are matters of judgment and opinion, and so many external factors affect conclusions, which might seem fairly satisfactory at any one time, that firm answers are scarcely possible. A current example will illustrate this problem. In view of the increasing costs of the war in Vietnam, should the federal government's expenditures for basic research be increased, or decreased, or held level? If the federal government makes any substantial decrease, how will it affect expenditures for basic research by non-government agencies? There are plenty of answers to these questions—the only trouble is that those answering are not even in substantial agreement.

Whether federal support of scientific research is adequate is a subject discussed endlessly, both in and out of the federal government, because, in the first place, it is of real importance to the government, industry, the universities and the nonprofit foundations from an over-all standpoint and to individual students and scientists as individuals; and, in the second place, no matter how much discussion there may be of the subject there is no possibility of arriving at consensus on a solution to the problems involved in it.

Probably, if careful analysis were to be made, we would find that majority opinion holds that federal support is inadequate. In the June 10, 1966, issue of *Science,* D. S. Greenberg had an article entitled "Money for Science: The Community Is Beginning To Hurt." His opening paragraphs are worth consideration:

There is a tendency among some scientists to equate the refusal of a grant with the persecution of Galileo. Thus, when research, like most wards of the federal treasury, must make a tithe to the Vietnam war, faculty club chatter often seems to suggest that science is going the way of Studebaker. Of course it isn't. In fact, the research community is bigger and richer than ever. [But] . . . while the research community is bigger, it is only slightly richer, and the disparity between size and support appears to be squeezing and, in some cases, stranding an indeterminate but possibly significant number of researchers.

Just what effect this is actually having on the condition and progress of American science is difficult to establish. The base line for doleful prognostication is high in the best of times. Furthermore, when it comes to specific cases, disappointed applicants usually prefer not to advertise their lack of success. Nevertheless, there are now innumerable indications of financial strains throughout the scientific community. Through two decades of training and construction programs, the federal government has created a vast population of consumers of research support, all imbued with the spirit of rising expectations. But now, because of the drain of the Vietnam war and the Johnson administration's order of priorities, apparently not enough federal money is being provided to support all their aspirations. And, as a result, some researchers are being left out altogether, while others are beginning to experience the scale of professional living normally associated with the English department.

. . .

At virtually every institution, there is considerable concern about the adequacy of funds for maintaining existing basic research programs or for carrying through with expansion programs now under way. This does not mean, however, that laboratories are being padlocked or that existing or planned programs are tapering off. Rather, it does mean that researchers, department heads, and deans are going through a laborious process of realigning priorities and seeking new sources of support.

There have been many statements from competent persons concerning the amount the United States as a nation *should* spend. As far back as 1945, Dr. Vannevar Bush, expressing his views five years before establishment of the National Science Foundation, estimated that such an agency would need $33.5 million for the first year of operation and $122.5 million for the fifth year. (In fact, the Foundation received only $3.5 million for its first full year of operation and $40.5 million for its fifth year of operation—not even an approximation of Bush's estimate.)

The report of the President's Scientific Research Board (the Steelman report) in 1947 recommended establishment of the Foundation with $50 million in support of basic research in its first year, rising to an annual rate of at least $250 million by 1957. (In fact, the Foundation did not receive a $50 million appropriation until 1958 nor $250 million until 1962.)

One way to determine how much should be spent for any purpose is to start with the total amount of funds available for all purposes, determine the relative amounts spent for each major purpose, and then make a subjective determination of the rightness of this distribution. The National Science Foundation compiles and publishes the data on research and development expenditures. U.S. gross national product (GNP)—the market value of the output of goods and services produced by the nation's economy—constitutes the funds available for all purposes, public and private. Frequently there are comparisons between the different amounts of GNP expended for these purposes. Of course, no one knows how much should be spent—we only know how much we have been spending. That amount is not inevitably the right amount.

The problem of "growth rate" of funds for research and development and for basic research is important and not easy to understand. Funds for basic research have been increasing more rapidly, on a percentage basis, than has the GNP. During the years 1953–58, early in the life of the National Science Foundation, the average annual increase in expenditures for basic research was 14.8 per cent, while the average annual increase rate for the GNP was only 5.1 per cent. This large difference has gradually been reduced, until in 1965–66 the rate for basic research was 10.5 per cent, while the GNP rate was 7.8 per cent. In the 1958–65 period, the highest rate of growth in basic research expenditures occurred—17 per cent.

It is important to note that no one person, no single agency of government, determined that the situations described in these two periods be established. Thousands of public and private sources made decisions on research and development expenditures with little or no attention to the size of the GNP or to what expenditures were being made by organizations other than their own.

For many years there has been considerable, although not unanimous, support for the principle that funds for basic research should increase by an amount equal to 15 per cent per year. One does not need to be a brilliant mathematician to realize that 15 per cent compound interest over a period of not too many years would produce a large sum. This did not, however, appear to daunt some early enthusiasts. Alan T. Waterman, then director of the National Science Foundation, was reported to have advocated, in 1961, an average rate of growth of 35 per cent per year for the next ten years, which would have produced an NSF budget of $5.3 billion for 1971. Two scientists of repute are reported to have advocated that the nation might devote to research and development as much as half of its gross national product by the end of the century. This result was obtained simply by projecting the existing rate of growth. John Lear cited these two examples in an article in the *Saturday Review,* April 1, 1967, which was extremely critical of "scientific pretension and exaggeration." He quoted Secretary of Health, Education, and Welfare John Gardner to the effect that "among all human enterprises" research "cannot hope to have the unique attribute of existing in a world without resource constraints."

An editorial in *Scientific Research* for July, 1967, discussed the National Science Foundation's need for more money. The editorial contained a quotation from a speech by Donald F. Hornig, the President's science adviser, and continued with comment on his remarks:

[Hornig said]: "The country need not be convinced any longer that we need strength in basic research. This is accepted by the Executive, the Congress, and by the people of the country. . . . What is *not* accepted is the notion that every part of science should grow at some automatic and predetermined rate, 15 per cent per year or any other number, as a consequence. . . ."

However sound and reasonable it may be to oppose an automatic and predetermined growth rate, we are confident that even Hornig would agree that a 3.1 per cent growth rate (represented by the House subcommittee's $495 million budget approved for NSF as compared with the final $480 million appropriated last year) is inadequate by any standards—inadequate even to keep up with the annual increase in the cost of working, let alone allow for any growth.

V

Primary Function:
The Promotion of Basic Research

If a history of the development of the Foundation's program activities were to be compiled, it would present a story of small beginnings followed by rapid growth in the number of programs, costs, and scope. A summary analysis of the principal elements is contained in House Report 1219 (1960):

a. Support of basic research and research facilities to sustain U.S. leadership in scientific progress, and to support thesis research which is a necessary part of graduate education;

b. Support of science education to maintain a supply of manpower adequate in quality as well as quantity to meet present and future national needs;

c. Support of institutions to facilitate internal balance in those already achieving excellence and to foster the growth and broad geographical distribution of additional centers;

d. Support of science information services to foster effective dissemination and use of scientific results by other scientists, engineers, and administrators;

e. Support of fact-gathering and analysis to aid NSF in its planning of internal operating policies and to aid other agencies, the President and the Congress in their planning of national policy.

The seven subsections of the act of 1950, which furnish the legal authority for the functions listed above, include two specifying the functions in paragraph (a) relating to the support or basic research. They stated that the Foundation was:

(2) to initiate and support basic scientific research and programs to strengthen scientific research potential in the mathematical, physical, medical, biological, engineering, and other
sciences, by making contracts or other arrangements (including
grants, loans, and other forms of assistance) to support such
scientific activities and to appraise the impact of research upon
industrial development and upon the general welfare;

(3) at the request of the Secretary of Defense, to initiate and
support specific scientific research activities in connection with
matters relating to the national defense by making contracts or
other arrangements (including grants, loans, and other forms
of assistance) for the conduct of such scientific research.

This broad grant of power has in practice adequately covered the various program activities the Foundation has devised, and individuals who spent so much effort writing the
original act are entitled to credit for their wisdom and fore-
sight in defining the research function in such a way that it
would not need frequent amendment to meet later developments.

The several basic research programs the Foundation has
established are of two types—support given to individuals
through project grants and support furnished to "big science"
through the national research programs, the national research
centers, and the financing of specialized research facilities. At
first, because funds available for grants were small, the Foundation was able to offer assistance to individuals. But it was
apparent that there were also many expensive projects requiring participation by numbers of scientists, engineers, and
technologists and the availability of elaborate facilities. The
idea of a researcher working alone in his laboratory is by no
means obsolete, but modern research in high energy physics,
to cite one example, demands far more personnel and equipment. "Little science" and "big science," if one wishes to call
them that, are not alternatives in any way, and few would care
to argue seriously that one or the other is more important. The
relative amount of support the Foundation should give to each
is a difficult and continuing policy problem, and not one that

can be decided once, for all time; every year when the budget is prepared, a determination has to be made again in dollars-and-cents terms, as Table 4 illustrates.

TABLE 4
Expenditures to Promote Basic Research
(in Millions of Dollars)

	1962	1963	1964	1965	1966
Basic research project support	$88.7	$107.2	$112.4	$119.5	$157.8
National research programs	12.3	17.1	25.9	42.2	36.0
National research centers	9.3	14.5	19.3	19.5	23.0
Specialized research facilities and support	46.8	23.8	19.6	27.7	28.3
TOTAL	$157.5	$162.7	$177.2	$208.9	$245.1

Most striking is the evidence of steady growth. The project support for individuals has nearly doubled; the national research programs have nearly tripled; the national research centers are using two-and-a-half times as much money. Only the programs for supplying specialized research facilities have decreased in amount, but such decreases are often more apparent than real and result from changes in the classifications used for budget purposes. (For example, expenditures for "university computational facilities and support" have appeared under "Science Education Support" in some NSF financial statements and under "Specialized Research Facilities" in others. This reclassification alone makes a difference of several million dollars. Engineering research has also been included under different subject headings.)

In this chapter, the programs supporting individual research and the three "big science" programs are described and their peculiar advantages and disadvantages discussed; the conduct of applied research, which the Foundation is increasingly being urged to support in certain areas as a necessary accompaniment to its major function of supporting basic research, is considered; and, in conclusion, the knotty problems of patents and the relationships between researcher and government in availing themselves of the advantages of a patent are touched upon.

BASIC RESEARCH PROJECT SUPPORT

One of the earliest decisions made by the Foundation was that its support for basic research would be distributed through the "project grant" method. The project grant system is easy to understand. An individual researcher presents his proposal to the Foundation, with a description of his project and its cost. After evaluation by experts, the Foundation considers all the individual requests, selecting for support those that are judged to have the most merit. The research grant is normally made to an institution for use by the scientist in the project he proposed. It may include funds for assistants or purchase of scientific equipment and partial reimbursement for indirect costs incurred by the institution. (The individual project grant method was not devised by the Foundation. It had been used by, among others, the Office of Naval Research, which, in many respects, furnished a pattern for the new foundation. The National Institutes of Health also have long made project grants in support of their programs of research.)

Although the administration of the Foundation's program of project grants for basic research is relatively simple, both for the Foundation and for the grantee, it does involve a number of important considerations. The decision, made immediately after the Foundation received its first appropriation, to support individual projects rather than to aid educational institutions or departments was, as noted earlier, dictated in part by necessity because the early appropriations were so small. But even more importantly, Office of Naval Research experience and the judgment of the majority of research scientists who were consulted favored the individual project grant.

The Foundation has always tried to distribute its support, including, of course, support to individual projects, taking into account the different fields of science, the different types of institutions, geographical distribution, proper consideration of promising young researchers, and assistance from other agencies. In practice, the Foundation must encourage proposals from all competent scientists who wish to receive grants. With the advice of expert committees in the various fields, a selection on the basis of the scientific merit of these proposals is made. Then, in order that the total program be truly national, final selections must be made from the approved projects taking into account all the considerations named above.

This policy-determination process is not only difficult but is also of the utmost importance, and its successful conduct is one of the major responsibilities of the Foundation. That the Foundation always succeeds is, of course, not true. Each individual researcher, each scientist in a particular field (which he thinks to be more important than all other fields), each college or university (and its concerned departments), and each region of the country may feel that its claim has been slighted through disproportionate amounts granted to projects in other categories.

In making project grants, as in carrying out all its functions, the Foundation must use utmost care not to exercise centralized control over science. The very basis of the individual project grant system is its extreme form of decentralization. It permits to a maximum degree the freedom and independent action in the choice and conduct of research necessary for scientific progress.

Director Waterman, who established the project grant system and had the unique experience of having to make it work, wrote in an article in *Science* (May 6, 1960):

The so-called "project method" of research support has a number of advantages. Properly interpreted, the plan is flexible and may be applied to narrowly defined problems in science or to broad areas. It enables the government to move in freely with the support needed for promising and significant undertakings of current interest. It provides for a national program in the sciences, utilizes the advice of the scientists in each field, and is based upon the significance and merit of the research proposed and the competence of the investigators. Since each grant and contract requires the official indorsement of the investigator's institution, the plan has evolved with the concurrence of the nation's universities and has had a most important indirect effect in helping to strengthen such institutions. In fact, such aid has often been of critical importance, particularly for the smaller schools.

The chief drawbacks of this method of research support are its failure thus far to provide full indirect costs and the difficulties it creates in departmental administration. It has also been criticized on the grounds that the reviewing process is slow and that the resulting program is too conservative.

In reply to these criticisms it can only be said that the slowness of the process is the price one pays for operating on the basis of consultation and advice, rather than "master-minding" the system from Washington. Probably it is offset by the great advantage of having the nation's scientific research and development problems widely understood by scientists as they participate in the solution of these problems.

Statistical description of the Foundation's program of individual project grants clearly demonstrates the rapid increase in the number of grants and the amounts expended on them, in the various fields and subfields of science within which the grants are made.

During its first year, 1950–51, the Foundation program of project grants was in process of establishment, and fiscal year 1952 was the first year of full operation. In that year, proposals amounting to $13.3 million were received, of which 8 per cent ($1.1 million) was approved. The limited funds at the Foundation's disposal had discouraged many competent investigators from submitting proposals, and the proportion of declined and withdrawn proposals was high in comparison with other federal agencies and private foundations because of the exceedingly stringent criteria for approval which had necessarily been adopted in view of the financial limitations. Although the program was relatively small in comparison with the total federal program, nearly 75 per cent of the dollar value of Foundation grants went to individuals from sponsoring institutions that had participated least in previous federal research support.

A complete account of the growth and development of this

program during the succeeding years would be interesting but
far too long for present purposes. Table 5 shows for the period

TABLE 5
Basic Research Project Support
(in Millions of Dollars)

	1962	1963	1964	1965	1966
Biological and medical sciences	$31.9	$38.4	$39.8	$41.6	$50.1
Mathematical, physical, and engineering sciences	45.1	59.9	—	—	—
Social sciences	7.7	9.0	9.0	10.0	12.2
Institutional grants*	3.7	—	—	—	—
International Science Act research	0.2	—	—	—	—
Mathematical and physical sciences	—	—	51.0	54.1	56.3
Engineering	—	—	12.6	13.7	18.0
Environmental sciences	—	—	—	—	21.1
TOTAL†	$88.7	$107.2	$112.4	$119.5	$157.8

* After 1962, the item institutional grants was made a separate heading.
† Owing to rounding off, totals may not equal sums of numbers above them.

1962–66 the grants by fields of science. In 1952, the Foundation had approved a little more than $1 million. In 1966, the
amount was over $157 million. Ninety-six grants were made
in 1952, 3,467 in 1966. Every field had received increased
funds, and new fields had been added. The Foundation has
repeatedly stated that its grants were being distributed equi-
tably on a geographical basis, and the Foundation's annual reports have presented supporting evidence.

Each annual report contains descriptions of project grants
to show the uses to which they are being put. A few examples,
selected to cover the fields of research represented, follow.

Grants in the Mathematical and Physical Sciences

In the 1966 report, a section on grants in the mathematical
and physical sciences opened with this statement: "The mathematical and physical sciences constitute the bedrock upon

which the entire scientific enterprise ultimately rests. About one-third of the Foundation support in basic research during fiscal year 1966 was in mathematics and the physical sciences, including astronomy, chemistry, and physics."

Descriptions of current projects included research in the exploding universe, the behavior of carbonium ions, image intensifiers, spectroscopic studies of energy transfer in molecules, energy levels of organic molecules, fixation of atmospheric nitrogen, a unique facility for nuclear structure physics research, a new 10-billion-volt electron synchroton, the radius of the pi-meson, and the relation of partial differential equations to the global properties of topological manifolds.

Grants in the Biological and Medical Sciences

The section on the biological and medical sciences in the 1966 report states:

> New concepts and techniques promise an understanding of life at more profound levels than had been previously thought possible.
>
> A new era in biology was opened in the 1950's with determination of the structure of DNA (. . . the molecular carrier of hereditary traits). Many of the remarkable and rapid achievements in molecular biology that occurred during this period were supported by the Foundation.
>
> As a result of the rapid advances in molecular biology, disciplinary boundaries are breaking down. . . . Increasingly, biologists are becoming oriented to the problems that must be solved irrespective of disciplinary boundaries—in fact more and more noteworthy advances are coming from multidisciplinary approaches.

Projects listed included research in juvenile hormones as insecticides, chemically influencing insect behavior, and controlling leaf metabolism.

Grants in the Environmental Sciences

The current upsurge of interest in the environmental sciences and the increase in the number and amount of project grants in these fields led the Foundation to establish in 1966 a new division of the environmental sciences, which includes atmospheric sciences, the solid earth sciences, and oceanography. Several examples of research findings were included in the 1966 annual report. Among them were global atmospheric circulation ("GHOST" balloon project, computer model of atmospheric flow) and origin and evolution of the Pacific Ocean Basin (age of the Pacific Ocean Basin, geological history of Midway Atoll).

Grants in Engineering

Although the Foundation was authorized in the act of 1950 to conduct basic scientific research in engineering, it has not made the number of grants nor allocated the amount of funds in this field that it has in some other areas. In the five-year period 1962–66, however, grants and funds for engineering sciences have more than doubled. The annual reports of the Foundation for 1965 and 1966 itemize the distribution of grants and funds under seven subheads. The 1966 report lists the subjects of these grants as dealing with separation and purification of chemicals, fluid turbulence, soil mechanics, design of earthquake-resistant structures, metallurgy, energy transfer (for example, plasmas, lasers, thermoelectric devices), materials processing, bioengineering, information theory, and operations research.

Grants in the Social Sciences

Although the National Science Foundation Act of 1950 did not include the social sciences in outlining five areas of basic research to be supported, differences of opinion developed over this matter, and a compromise formula was devised to permit such activity at the discretion of the Foundation without making it obligatory. This was done by adding to the five named fields of research (mathematical, physical, medical, biological, and engineering) the term "other sciences." The anthropological sciences have received the most grants and the most money, with the sociological sciences coming second.

The first grants for economic and social geography and for political science were made in 1966.

The Foundation's annual report for 1966 justified support of the social sciences in these words:

> The basic research supported by the Foundation in [the social sciences] seeks to identify and analyze that most complex of all relationships, the relationships among individuals and among social groups. To the degree that it is successful these scientists provide knowledge that can be used to make technological change more acceptable to society. Man must not only know his world in order to better it, he must know himself. The past year has brought renewed attention to this effort.

Some of the projects reported on were committee decision-making, child-rearing in different cultures, laboratory "games," analysis of international trade, food-gathering in a primitive society, and the effectiveness of language in communication.

Big Science: The National Research Programs

Although the origin of the term "big science" is uncertain, what it describes is very definite. Since the end of World War II, new subjects and methods of scientific research have increasingly required the use of very costly equipment and of organized groups of specialists. Radio astronomy, and studies of the earth's crust, to name two, are indeed "big science."

Fortunately, the grant of authority in the act of 1950 was sufficiently broad so that no new powers were needed to permit the National Science Foundation to support such projects. Additional specific legislation did, however, authorize support of research in weather modification (1958) and research in marine resources (1966).

One section in the Act of 1950 (1873(c)) had an important relationship to big science projects. This was the section that said, "The Foundation shall not, itself, operate any laboratories or pilot plants." In 1945, Dr. Vannevar Bush had established the principle, saying that a science agency "should promote research through contracts or grants to organizations outside the federal government. It should not operate any laboratories of its own."

Other departments and agencies of the federal government maintain a large number of laboratories, but this prohibition appears to have been sufficiently satisfactory and workable in the case of the Foundation, and few, if any, attempts have been made to change it. However, the need for major facilities for basic research purposes has made it necessary to use the contract method of supporting the construction and operation of such facilities, and contracts have been made with groups of individuals working on large-scale projects. Some of the national research programs, the national research centers, and large-scale facilities for basic research are examples of projects operated under contract.

The problems involved in NSF support of the large-scale programs and centers even though they are not directly operated by the Foundation, are numerous. The planning and administration of big science projects make quite different demands on the Foundation's staff from those made by the planning and administration of individual project grants. There are major questions of long-range policy and funding involved in the very large, very expensive projects. Once such a project is initiated, its continuance for many years—perhaps permanently—may be expected. The NSF staff may find too much of its time and attention occupied with this part of its work, and often it is hard to recruit and keep the top management experts needed. If there are many huge, complex projects, so much money will have to be used for them each year that other activities of the Foundation may be starved, or it may be impossible to add any new large projects—no matter how desirable they may be. About one-half of the total amount of funds for basic research support has been used for big science expenditures.

Many members of Congress have become concerned about these problems because of their budget decisions concerning total NSF funds and their distribution among the different activities. When, in 1965, the House Committee on Science and

Astronautics, through its Subcommittee on Science, Research, and Development, held extensive hearings on all aspects of the operations of the Foundation, it observed in its final report that

> Congress, when it considers proposals from the Foundation, and from other agencies for major new scientific and technical facilities, should inquire about: (a) the expected operating lifetime; (b) the best estimate of operating and other capital funds to be required throughout the years; and (c) the circumstances under which the installation ultimately should be retired from active service.
>
> As for NSF administration of big science projects, the subcommittee is not persuaded that NSF responsibilities extend only to selecting among proposals and making and auditing expenditures. The Foundation has a responsibility for its national laboratories and for large projects. It would seem that NSF should have a competence, through its own staff or through others, to periodically assess the quality of work and administration of such undertakings. In particular, for a direct NSF operation such as Project Mohole, the Foundation should have a sufficiently strong engineering capability to independently review the major decisions and approvals required during the course of a "big-science" project. NSF organization for big science projects must certainly be properly structured so as not to detract from top management attention to other of its program.

The committee report continued with observations on three of the big science projects—weather modification, Project Mohole, and computers for universities—with discussion of the problems peculiar to each.

The obvious conclusion concerning the future of the Foundation and big science is that as science gets even bigger, the Foundation will have to continue to make major policy decisions and administrative changes to cope with this expanding function. But Congress, the universities, and the entire scientific community are deeply and directly involved in these problems, and the Foundation acting alone cannot be expected to solve them. In recent years, the National Science Foundation has assumed constantly increasing responsibility for broad scientific programs in which several federal departments and agencies participate, often with nongovernmental agencies, and frequently with other nations. As the one federal agency primarily concerned with basic research, it has appeared to be the appropriate organization to coordinate and handle the financial aspects of U.S. contributions to the so-called national research programs.

Frequently, the scientific community, acting through the National Academy of Sciences, has been the source of a proposal that the United States should participate in a project. A national research program usually has a limited budget and a definite purpose. Typically, each consists of a variety of basic research projects centered around a single theme and grouped by area of special interest rather than scientific field. The funds are usually disbursed to universities for use of scientists, and thus they are, in effect, supplements to individual project grants. In some cases, the Foundation has broad authority under its legislation to assume responsibility for a national program, but more often specific legislation or an executive order, particularly for international programs, provides the necessary mandate.

The National Science Foundation has designated the following as national research programs:

	Fiscal year
International Geophysical Year	1957–58
Antarctic research program	1958–
Weather modification	1960–
Deep crustal studies of the earth (Project Mohole)	1961–66
International Indian Ocean expedition	1962–
United States–Japan cooperative science program	1963–
International years of the quiet sun	1963–
Ocean sediment coring program	1966–

Table 6 shows the amounts obligated to these programs for the period 1962–66.

TABLE 6
Financial Obligations for National Research Programs, 1962–66
(in Millions of Dollars)

	1962	1963	1964	1965	1966
Antarctic research program*	$7.2	$6.4	$7.2	$7.6	$8.4
Indian Ocean expedition*	2.1	4.4	4.9	3.7	1.1
Weather modification†	1.3	1.3	1.5	2.0	1.9
International years of the quiet sun*	—	1.0	3.7	3.5	1.6
Ocean sediment coring program†	—	—	—	—	5.4
Deep crustal studies of the earth†	1.7	3.3	8.0	24.7	17.0
U.S.–Japan cooperative science program*	—	0.7	0.7	0.7	0.7
TOTAL	$12.3	$17.1	$26.0	$42.2	$36.1

* A national program of an international nature of the Federal Council for Science and Technology.
† A domestic program.

These programs are of three types. The International Geophysical Year, the Antarctic research program, the international Indian Ocean expedition, the U.S.–Japan cooperative science program, and the international years of the quiet sun are, or have been, among the so-called national programs of the Federal Council for Science and Technology, through which the United States participates in an international program under the auspices of intergovernmental or international science organizations. A second group is composed entirely of domestic programs (weather modification, deep crustal studies of the earth, the ocean sediment coring program) of a basic research nature, not clearly related to the purposes of any one federal agency. A third group of programs, in which the promise of public interest appears to justify federal support, is designated by the President or the Federal Council and includes atmospheric sciences, high-energy physics, materials research, oceanography, and water resources research.

The National Science Foundation has primary responsibility for conducting the first two groups of programs. In the third type, it participates as one among many agencies, and interagency committees under the council develop goals and policies and designate agency responsibilities. The financing of this third type of national program is complicated. For example, in fiscal year 1966 the following agencies contributed to the program for atmospheric sciences: the departments of Agriculture, Commerce, Defense, the Interior, and Health, Education, and Welfare, the Atomic Energy Commission, the Federal Aviation Agency (now the Federal Aviation Administration), the National Aeronautics and Space Administration, and the National Science Foundation.

The programs involving international science activities constitute an important part of the Foundation's work, and there has been more general public interest in them—particularly in the International Geophysical Year—than in most of the Foundation's other programs. They are discussed in full in Chapter IX.

The published list of grants and awards made to the national research programs in fiscal year 1966 can be analyzed to yield several different kinds of information. Almost half of the grants and awards went to the Antarctic research program. They were given to institutions in 2 foreign countries, 28 American states, and the District of Columbia. The numbers of grants by states in other programs were for weather modification, 17; U.S.–Japan cooperative science program, 15; international years of the quiet sun, 13; deep crustal studies of the earth, 5; Indian Ocean expedition, 6; ocean sediment coring program, 1.

The amounts of grants varied widely, as a few examples illustrate: the U.S. Department of Commerce, for construction of an Antarctic trawler, $874,500; the University of Illinois, for a symposium on social and economic aspects of weather modification, $2,900; and the U.S. Department of the Interior, for geophysical studies of Pacific volcanoes, phase I, $4,500.

In a large proportion of cases, the grants and awards were made to individuals through a college or university; many were made to government departments and agencies; others, to research institutions and industries. Under "deep crustal studies of the earth," most of the grants were for work on Project Mohole. The largest, $16.6 million, was to Brown and Root, Inc. of Houston, Texas, the prime contractor on the project. Other grants were made to the University of California at San Diego, the Smithsonian Institution, the National Academy of Sciences, Astrafilms, Inc. (Maryland), and M. Rosenblatt and Son, Inc. (New York). How much was expended is not indicated, but the termination of Project Mohole was accompanied by the recovery of certain unexpended funds.

Of the three domestic national research programs—in weather modification, deep crustal studies of the earth, and ocean sediment coring—one is defunct, and famous. That is the program in deep crustal studies, more familiarly known during its short, much-debated life as Project Mohole.

Project Mohole

The NSF program of deep crustal studies of the earth was one of the most ambitious earth science projects ever planned. Project Mohole was an attempt to probe through three miles of the ocean and three miles of the earth's crust to the unexplored mantle below. The technical problems were formidable, but the scientific world believed that such a major venture into pure scientific research was well worth the effort. So much was written about it that the general public was kept well informed on the purposes of the project, its progress, the difficulties encountered, and, finally, the reasons why Congress refused in 1966 to grant more funds for its support.

Mohole's inception was credited to an informal group of scientists calling themselves the "American Miscellaneous Society." By the end of 1957, the society had become affiliated with the National Academy of Sciences, as the AMSOC Committee. In the following years this committee and the Foundation jointly carried on the Mohole planning. For some time, there was no single point of responsibility, the post of Mohole Project Director not being created until 1964. When actual operations began, the drilling through the mantle was turned over to a prime contractor, Brown and Root, Inc., of Houston. Controversy as to the suitability of this firm and the NSF method of selecting it soon erupted and continued.

In 1966, Congress refused to authorize further funds for Project Mohole. The reasons for this action were many and complex. The House Committee on Appropriations, in reporting on the NSF budget, commented:

> In view of the current world situation and the need to continually review priorities, the Committee has not allowed funds for Project Mohole. This project has progressed slowly with considerable difficulty—the total estimated cost is in excess of $75,000,000. The cost of the project has already greatly exceeded the original estimate and promises to increase still further. The Committee suggests that funds of the Foundation can be more advantageously used in other activities and no funds are included to continue this project.

During the course of the appropriations measure through the House and the Senate, extensive debate occurred over the discontinuance of Project Mohole. In the House, several members expressed disapproval of the cut, but no amendment was proposed to restore the amount, and the bill was passed with no item for deep crustal studies. The Senate Committee on Appropriations, however, recommended restoration of the full amount of $19.7 million, stating its belief that it would be a serious mistake to suspend the project and would involve a tremendous loss of prestige and progress. But even here, Senator Gordon Allott (Colorado) filed his individual views, dissenting from the action of the Committee in recommending the restoration of funds, saying, "in view of the present state of our economy and the desire of all in government to hold costs down as far as possible—I do not believe that Project Mohole is justifiable, and I will not agree to including funds for its continuation." Senator Allott presented an amendment providing that the Foundation should use none of its funds for Mohole, and cutting the entire appropriation for it. Senator Magnuson and five other senators spoke in opposition to the amendment. On a roll-call vote, thirty-seven senators were for the amendment, forty-six against it, and seventeen did not vote. Thus, the amendment was lost and funds for Mohole retained. But then the Committee on Conference, appointed to reconcile the different version passed by the two houses, could not reach agreement. Finally, both houses agreed to omission of the appropriation for Project Mohole, and the President signed the bill on September, 1966.

Science (which is published by the American Association for the Advancement of Science) covered the progress of adoption of the NSF budget thoroughly and consistently took a position of strong support for continuation of Project Mohole. An editorial on June 3, 1966, stated emphatically:

> On the surface, what is involved is a delay on a contract for a drilling platform. This would "save" about $20 million in fiscal 1967. In fact, what is involved is forfeiture of world leadership in exploration and exploitation of the deep-sea bottom. What is at stake are trillions of dollars worth of resources.

In September, 1966, when the Foundation began to close down the project, some subcontracts that were nearly completed were allowed to run on, but work on the construction of the drilling platform was stopped. The 1966 annual report of the National Science Foundation contained a very brief statement about the termination of Project Mohole, a part of which is quoted:

> At the time the project was discontinued, most of the research and development work had been completed, but construction of of the drilling platform and fabrication of certain other equipment were in their very early stages. A number of significant contributions in the field of engineering had already resulted from the work completed. These will undoubtedly have a considerable impact on the drilling industry, and on the possible development of stable platforms for heavy work at sea. Among these contributions are the design and model-testing of the unique Mohole drilling platform and of the platform positioning system; the design, fabrication, and testing of a coring turbo-drill and the design and fabrication of the prototype of a revolu-

tionary retractable diamond coring bit; the design and fabrication of a deep-ocean untended digital data acquisition system; and the design of a method of sonar hole reentry.

In its issue of May 12, 1967, *Science* magazine noted that there appeared to be little hope for reviving Project Mohole, particularly in view of the tightness of the federal research budgets.

The Ocean Sediment Coring Program

A new item in the National Science Foundation budget for fiscal year 1966, with an appropriation of $5.4 million, provided for a joint effort by several major oceanographic institutions to obtain long cores of the sediments comprising the upper layers of the earth's suboceanic crust. Facetiously called the "poor man's Mohole," this project was planned to yield information on the age of the ocean basins, the earth's climatic history, the origin, history, and structure of the continental shelf, and possible new mineral and petroleum resources. Both the scientific objectives and the participants were closely related to Project Mohole—the early phases of which had demonstrated the feasibility of obtaining continuous cores of sediments from the ocean floor by using a conventional well-drilling vessel, suitably modified for dynamic positioning in deep water. The first step was to charter an existing drilling vessel to be modified for deep-sea operations.

In January, 1967, the Foundation contracted with the Scripps Institution of Oceanography to undertake the project. One of the criticisms of Mohole had been that the Foundation had tried to carry out that project itself. In addition to the fiscal year 1966 obligation, $1.3 million was allocated in 1967, and the Foundation requested an additional $3.0 million for 1968. These funds were to cover the costs of initial ship operations, core analysis, and related programs, with actual drilling operations to begin during calendar year 1968.

Some of the major systems and pieces of equipment used in

Project Mohole are still expected to be useful in the ocean sediment coring program, with substantial cost savings to the government. Core samples will be distributed to all interested and qualified scientists for detailed studies, and it is anticipated that their studies will lead to a fundamental advance in man's knowledge of the ocean basins and of the earth as a whole.

Weather Modification

The NSF's weather modification program was created by adding a new paragraph to the legislation describing the functions of the Foundation (1862(a)(9)): "to initiate and support a program of study, research, and evaluation in the field of weather modification, giving particular attention to areas that have experienced floods, drought, hail, lightning, fog, tornadoes, hurricanes, or other weather phenomena, and to report annually to the President and the Congress thereon." In addition, a new section setting forth details concerning research contracts, gifts, hearings, and so on, for weather modification was added. The Foundation was instructed to consult with meteorologists and scientists in private life and with agencies of government interested in, or affected by, experimental research in this field. The background of this legislation involved several studies whose conclusions had indicated the need to designate some agency to promote and support research in weather modification. After enactment of the 1958 legislation, the Foundation expended over a million dollars the next year alone on weather modification studies. Since then, reports in 1966 by the Special Commission on Weather Modification and by the Panel on Weather and Climate Modification of the National Academy of Sciences have both emphasized the need for increased activity.

One particularly striking study, designated Project Hailsworth, involved cooperative hail research during the summer of 1966. Twenty-three separate research teams pooled their facilities and talents to concentrate on the same hailstorms in the Great Plains area, and twelve representative storms were studied, in what the Foundation described as

> . . . a unique experiment to determine whether a community effort of scientists could be successfully organized and carried to completion. Approximately 12 aircraft and 81 technical and scientific personnel demonstrated the feasibility of assembling a critical mass of manpower and facilities to study a large storm system of considerable complexity and extent.

The National Center for Atmospheric Research contributed aircraft, radar sets, a high-gain antenna, and other items of support equipment, and seven of their scientists participated in the field experiments.

As required by law, the Foundation published a regulation, effective January 1, 1966, requiring that notice must be given of intent to modify the atmosphere, at least thirty days prior to actual field operations and that specified reports and records must be kept. As of June 30, 1966 notification of ninety-two projects had been filed with the NSF.

Administration of the weather modification program is vested in a program director in the section for atmospheric sciences in the division of environmental sciences. He is assisted by advisory panels consisting of six members each on atmospheric sciences and on weather modification.

In 1966, $1,851,381 was used for support of the national research programs for weather modification. Thirty-three grants were made—five for projects in California; three each for Arizona, Colorado, Massachusetts, New Mexico, and New York; two for Illinois and Pennsylvania; and one each for the District of Columbia, Missouri, Nebraska, Nevada, North Dakota, Oklahoma, South Dakota, Texas, and Washington. Many of these were made to universities for projects to be undertaken by their staffs. Grants also went to the Douglas Aircraft Company, The Rand Corporation, the National Academy of Sciences, Arthur D. Little, Inc., and other non-academic, nonprofit agencies.

Coordination of the Foundation's weather modification activities with those of the numerous federal departments and agencies that also have such programs is described in Chapter XI.

National Programs of the Federal Council for Science and Technology

The basic research programs involving the operations of several federal departments and agencies, including the National Science Foundation, in carrying out important national functions not the primary responsibility of any one of them are described in *Special Analyses, Budget of the United States, Fiscal Year 1968*. How these programs are funded is summarized briefly, below.

Atmospheric sciences are financed chiefly by the Department of Defense and the National Aeronautics and Space Administration. The research involves meteorology relating to the earth's atmosphere, aeronomy relating to earth's upper atmosphere, and planetary atmospheres relating to extraterrestrial atmospheres. NASA space flights account for a major part of the costs.

Space programs also involved large expenditures for research, other than in the atmospheric sciences, in 1966, by the Department of Defense ($1.7 million) and the National Aeronautics and Space Administration ($5.1 million).

Medical research accounted for $823.8 million expended by the Public Health Service in the Department of Health, Education, and Welfare in 1966, but six other departments and agencies expended $343.5 million.

Marine science and technology research involved eleven departments and agencies in 1966, with the departments of Defense ($174.9 million) and the Interior ($56.5 million) and the National Science Foundation ($47.7 million) as the major participants.

Water research is carried out chiefly by the Department of the Interior ($63.0 million in 1966).

It will be noted that the National Science Foundation, a participant in all these programs, has a major responsibility *only* in marine science and technology. In most cases, the research costs are borne chiefly by those departments and agencies having special interest in the particular programs because they relate to their respective functions. (See Table 7.)

TABLE 7
Financial Obligations for Selected Programs of the Federal Council for Science and Technology, 1966
(in Millions of Dollars)

Program	All Departments and Agencies	National Science Foundation
Atmospheric sciences		
Meteorology	$113.3	$11.3
Aeronomy	74.2	1.6
Planetary atmospheres	21.0	2.6
Total	208.5	15.5
Medical research		
Conduct of	1,102.5	*
Facilities	64.8	*
Total	1,167.3	24.2
Marine science and technology	333.4	47.2
Space programs	7,007.9	3.2
Water research	90.4	1.9
TOTAL	$8,807.5	$92.0

* Not included.

National Research Centers

In 1954, the Foundation formed an advisory panel to develop a "national program" in radio astronomy, for the first time carrying into effect an idea that had been under consideration for some time. Although the Foundation is prohibited from the operation of any laboratories or pilot plants, early in its existence it recognized the need for major research facilities in different scientific fields, which would be available, as public facilities, to qualified scientists. There are, to be sure, several large astronomical observatories, not federally supported, but they are not generally available to all competent researchers and, in any event, already operate at full capacity. Few universities would be able to afford the costs of construction of such installations and the costs of operation for the universities' sole use, but the device used by the Atomic Energy Commission presented a new organizational form for the conduct of very large-scale basic research. Their laboratories at Los Alamos, Argonne, and Brookhaven are managed by a university, a group of universities, or an industrial concern under contract to the federal government and, in general, are engaged in both basic and applied research. Following the AEC lead, the National Science Foundation in 1956 established its first National Research Center, the National Radio Astronomy Observatory at Green Bank, West Virginia. It is operated by Associated Universities, Inc., under contract with the Foundation.

In all, four national research centers have been created by the Foundation. Table 8 indicates the joint university organization that operates each of them and gives the pertinent financial statistics. Three of these centers are used for astronomical research and one for atmospheric research. The former provide large and costly telescopes and associated equipment

TABLE 8
Financial Obligations of National Research Centers, 1957–66
(in Millions of Dollars)

Fiscal Year	National Radio Astronomy Observatory*	Kitt Peak National Observatory†	Cerro-Tololo Inter-American Observatory†	National Center for Atmospheric Research‡
1957	$4.0	—	—	—
1958	1.1	$3.1	—	—
1959	4.4	4.4	—	—
1960	1.0	0.8	—	$0.5
1961	5.4	2.0	—	0.5
1962	5.7	2.9	$0.05	1.1
1963	4.6	3.8	1.0	5.2
1964	4.6	4.4	1.0	9.3
1965	3.4	6.9	1.4	7.8
1966	4.9	6.2	1.4	10.5

* Operated by Associated Universities, Inc.
† Operated by the Association of Universities for Research in Astronomy, Inc.
‡ Operated by the University Corporation for Atmospheric Research.

for the use of the scientific community at large. They are staffed by a limited number of outstanding resident astronomers and by the requisite number of engineers, technicians, and service personnel. The resident astronomers give continuity and cohesiveness to the program and do advance planning for new facilities, as well as contributing to the research itself. However, a majority of the time available on the telescopes is assigned to visiting astronomers and graduate students, the selection being based on the scientific promise of the work that they propose to do.

The National Radio Astronomy Observatory at Green Bank, West Virginia, is located on a site chosen to avoid as much as possible electromagnetic interference of all types. The facilities are so delicate that even the ignition systems of passing automobiles affect them, and additional land has had to be acquired to increase their isolation. More than 200 persons constitute the staff. Over one-half of the observing time on the telescopes is taken by visiting astronomers. The research programs conducted at this observatory are of a highly technical nature and include radio telescope design studies and a large variety of radio, millimeter-wave, and infrared measurements of planetary, stellar, and galactic sources. In addition to the major installation at Green Bank, the headquarters, the computer division, and some administrative offices are located at Charlottesville, Virginia.

The Kitt Peak National Observatory is located forty-five miles from Tucson, Arizona, on 6,875-foot-high Kitt Peak, with supporting laboratories, shops, and administrative offices in Tucson. There are more than 200 staff members at this observatory, which specializes in optical astronomy. The work is carried out under three divisions—stellar, solar, and space. In 1966, the McMath solar telescope, the largest in the world, was used by 16 visitors, five of whom were graduate students, and by three foreign visitors. Forty-one visiting astronomers, including four from outside the United States and sixteen graduate students, used the stellar telescopes. The space facilities were used by five visiting scientists, including one for whom an Aerobee rocket system was provided and a payload integrated. Advanced graduate students use telescope observing time at Kitt Peak in preparation of their Ph.D. theses, and, in addition, the observatory conducts a summer research assistant program, which has enrolled forty-four students from twenty-six universities in five years of operation. The students are primarily first-year and second-year, carefully selected, graduate students who work with the resident staff.

The third of the Foundation's astronomical observatories, the Cerro-Tololo Inter-American Observatory, is located on a 7,200-foot mountain in the foothills of the Andes Mountains about 300 miles north of Santiago, Chile, with administrative headquarters in the coastal city of La Serena, about 60 miles from the telescope. This observatory is the counterpart in the Southern Hemisphere of Kitt Peak National Observatory in the Northern Hemisphere. Among the interesting celestial objects that can be studied there are the Magellanic Clouds (the nearest external galaxies) and some of the largest and nearest star clusters. The center of the Milky Way passes nearly overhead at the latitude of Cerro Tololo. Telescopes previously existing in the Southern Hemisphere were not modern instruments, not located in astronomically favorable climates, and not regularly available to U.S. astronomers. With the cooperation of the Chilean government, a three-year survey was conducted to choose a site. Cerro Tololo was chosen, and construction began in 1963. It was well along in 1966. The not-for-profit Association of Universities for Research in Astronomy (AURA, Inc.), which operates the Kitt Peak National Observatory, also operates Cerro Tololo, and the dean of the College of Physical Sciences and Mathematics of the University of Chile has been appointed a member of its board of directors.

The increased national research effort in the atmospheric sciences led the Foundation to establish its fourth center, the National Center for Atmospheric Research (NCAR), with the purpose of studying the large-scale behavior of the earth's atmosphere. The NCAR has its permanent laboratories on

Table Mountain near Boulder, Colorado, with more than 400 staff members. Research programs are centered in the Laboratory of Atmospheric Sciences (LAS) and the High Altitude Observatory (HAO). The LAS program emphasizes the general circulation and motions of the atmosphere, the life cycles of trace gases and aerosols in the atmosphere, and the physics of clouds and precipitation. The HAO is concerned with the sun, the solar atmosphere, and the region between the sun and earth. The NCAR Facilities Laboratory is responsible for ballooning, aviation, computing, and field observation including sites, equipment, and technical staff to assist visiting scientists.

In addition to conducting its own research programs and supporting university research projects, the NCAR participates in a number of atmospheric research projects conducted by government agencies, university scientists, and other national and international research groups. Weather modification research and large-scale meteorological experiments occupy much of the time of the NCAR staff.

The advanced study program conducted by the National Center for Atmospheric Research promotes the broad view of the atmospheric sciences necessary in solving many basic problems, and it helps to define specific problems of urgency. Post-doctoral appointments and an affiliate professorship program are parts of the advanced study program. The fellowship program, in its third year, offers a year of graduate study in atmospheric sciences and a summer research appointment at the National Center for Atmospheric Research.

Specialized Research Facilities

In its annual report for 1956, the National Science Foundation stated:

As time goes on, it is anticipated that the future progress of research will depend in some fields of science upon an increasing ratio of research tools to scientific manpower. Production of necessary particles for research in nuclear physics, for example, is dependent upon equipment such as the nuclear accelerator and the nuclear reactor, all elaborate and costly devices. Acceleration of progress in many scientific and engineering fields through application of the electronic computer to complicated and extensive problems will require increasing numbers of computers of high speed and large memory capacity. Furthering of research on the nature and characteristics of the universe requires highly specialized astronomical equipment in locations favorable for such studies. In addition, the forwarding of research on the nature of life itself—the province of biology—requires modern laboratory equipment in locations favorable to studying life forms in their natural habitats. In all of these areas, and in other areas which may emerge, the national interest requires that adequate means be available for assisting scientists to perform research to the limits of their ability.

Since its beginning, the Foundation had made grants to provide necessary equipment and facilities to aid in carrying out basic research. The earliest grants were small, but increases both in the total amounts and in their relative importance were rapid in the following years and are still increasing. For example, there were 184 grants in 1965 and 214 in 1966, with an increase of more than a half-million dollars obligated. Table 9 contains the amounts of grants for the years from 1962 to 1966.

By 1955, many problems and difficulties involved in making grants for specialized physical facilities for scientific research had developed. In 1956, at the request of the Bureau of the Budget, the Foundation prepared a special report on the current status and future needs for research facilities. It concluded that federal support would have to be provided for the facilities and, in some cases, for their operation and maintenance. It would be difficult to establish criteria applicable in all cases, but certain specified factors should be taken into consideration in each individual case.

The principles established in 1956 remain substantially unchanged today, even though the program has grown rapidly, with Congressional approval, until it exceeded $28 million in 1966. There are five principal areas within which grants are made for specialized research facilities—biological, physical,

Alan T. Waterman, director of the NSF, 1950–64.

Vannevar Bush at about the time his *Science: The Endless Frontier* was published. This report was instrumental in the establishment of the National Science Foundation. *Harris & Ewing, Washington, D.C.*

Leland J. Haworth, director of the NSF since 1964.

Entomologists from Bishop Museum, Hawaii, measure the microclimate around a site inhabited by springtails (primitive insects related to silverfish), which live under rocks in many ice-free areas of Antarctica, to determine under what conditions insects can survive and to find clues about the origin of Antarctic insects. *NSF photo*

A Stanford University biologist examines a 4-foot-long, 50-pound *Dissostichus mawsoni* taken from the mouth of a seal that caught it in the depths of ice-covered McMurdo Sound. Scientists kept the unusual fish alive for ten days as part of an investigation of the physiology and cold-adaptation mechanisms of Antarctic fish. *NSF photo*

As part of U.S., Soviet, and British cosmic ray research, a Bartol Foundation physicist makes adjustments on an antenna that transmits "forward scatter" signals from McMurdo Station to the Soviet base Vostok. A network of such antennas to study cosmic rays was established at U.S., Soviet, and British stations by the National Bureau of Standards. *NSF photo*

Members of the Japanese Antarctic research group examine fish caught in a trap just pulled out of McMurdo Sound. *NSF photo*

Kitt Peak National Observatory, Arizona. *Kitt Peak Nat'l Obs. photo*

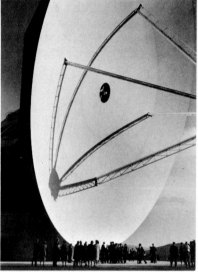

National Radio Astronomy Observatory, Green Bank, West Virginia. *NSF photo*

National Center for Atmospheric Research, Boulder, Colorado. *NCAR photo*

Portion of Cerro Tololo Inter-American Observatory in the Andes Mountains in Chile. *Kitt Peak Nat'l Obs. photo*

This laboratory devoted to radiation studies at the University of California (Berkeley) is one of many supported by NSF funds.

Postdoctoral fellowships supported by the NSF may be devoted to work such as that in electron microscopy being pursued at the Massachusetts Institute of Technology.

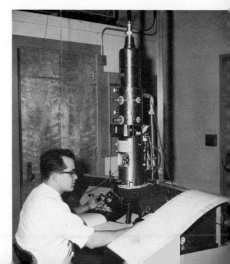

While attending an NSF-sponsored institute in chemistry and physics at Northern Illinois University, elementary-school teachers learn how to use a simple airplane model to demonstrate Bernoulli's theorem of flight.

A high school physical-science teacher participates in an NSF-sponsored summer research program at the U.S. Navy Electronics Laboratory in San Diego, California. *Official photograph, U.S. Navy*

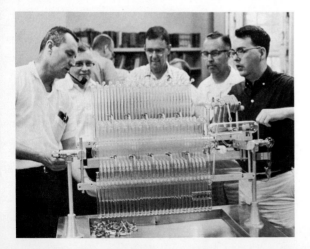

College teachers observe a demonstration of the separation of iron, cobalt, and nickel at an NSF-funded institute at Emory University, Georgia. *Wiley Perry*

These children are participating in a science curriculum improvement study supported by the NSF and conducted by the Physics Department of the University of California (Berkeley).

High school students gather marine specimens on a California beach at an NSF summer institute in oceanography and mathematics held at Humboldt State College, Arcata, California. *News and Information Service, Humboldt State College*

Dr. D. S. Kothari (left), eminent physicist and chairman of the University Grants Commission of India, and Dr. N. E. Bingham examine a physics textbook produced in India with the aid of an NSF grant.

Programs funded by the NSF have ranged from a computerized urban-renewal study conducted by economists at the University of Washington (above) to marine research in the Indian Ocean involving forty-one vessels from thirteen nations (the research ship U.S.S. *Anton Bruun* is shown below) with scientists from twenty-eight nations participating.

TABLE 9
Financial Obligations for Specialized Research Facilities, 1962–66
(in Millions of Dollars)

Type of Facility	1962	1963	1964	1965	1966
Graduate research laboratory	$26.1	—	—	—	—
Specialized biological research	3.1	$3.5	$3.5	$3.5	$3.5
University computing	3.0	5.0	4.5	4.5	—
Academic computational	—	—	—	—	8.9
Physical science research	8.7	9.3	5.7	15.3	7.3
Oceanography research	5.9	5.9	5.0	3.0	2.4
Specialized social science	—	0.2	1.0	0.2	0.8
Engineering research	—	—	—	1.3	1.2
Specialized research equipment	—	—	—	—	4.2
TOTAL	$46.8	$23.9	$19.7	$27.8	$28.2

environmental, engineering, and social sciences. Grants for university computing facilities are, in fact, like the specialized research facilities grants, but they are included in the institutional grants programs.

An example or two of each of the five types of grant will indicate their importance in the conduct of research.

Biological science research facilities. In 1964, a grant was made to the University of Michigan to aid in the construction of an all-weather aquatic biology laboratory at the University's field station, permitting experimental testing of data obtained in field studies.

Oceanographic research facilities. The 1965 report of the Foundation described the *Alpha Helix,* the first U.S. vessel devoted to marine physiological investigations. The Scripps Institution of Oceanography, with a grant from the National Science Foundation, spent five years in the design and construction of the vessel. During 1966, it operated off the coast of Australia in the area of the Great Barrier Reef; during

1967 it carried out a program in the Amazon River basin; and in 1968 an expedition to northern latitudes was scheduled.

The Foundation also assists in financing shore facilities. A 1963 survey revealed the pressing needs for better facilities and equipment for marine biology and biological oceanography. Few of the existing marine stations had sufficiently modern buildings and equipment to support first-rate research programs, and current Foundation grants are aimed to improve this condition.

Physical science facilities. The first of these to be supported, in 1965, were chemistry research instruments. Modern methods have made it necessary to employ expensive, highly specialized new instruments including infrared, ultraviolet, mass, nuclear magnetic resonance, and electron spin resonance spectrometers, and gas chromatographic equipment.

University astronomy research facilities receiving grants have included highly complex interferometers for radio astronomy, which the California Institute of Technology constructed with Foundation aid. Several outstanding contributions have been made with these facilities, even before construction was complete. Discovery of the magnetic field of Jupiter and determination of the radio positions of quasars were two of them.

University nuclear physics facilities and university physics research facilities are expensive necessities that the Foundation has supported with increasing amounts of grants, contracting, for example, with Cornell University to build an electron accelerator with an energy of 10 billion electron volts (BeV) at an estimated cost of $11.3 million. Upon completion, planned for 1968, this accelerator will produce the highest available electron energies of any except the Stanford University Linear Accelerator, which is designed to operate at 20 BeV; the Cornell version has certain superior research advantages.

University atmospheric research facilities have recently received more grants and more funds, as this area of research has been expanding rapidly. In 1964, fourteen grants were made; in 1965, seventeen; and in 1966, nineteen. One grant was made to the Irving Langmuir Laboratory for Atmospheric Research, part of the New Mexico Institute of Mining and Technology. This laboratory is located on top of a 10,000-foot mountain from which approximately 20,000 square miles of desert, steppe, and mountain terrain can be studied by radar, photographically, and visually.

Engineering research facilities. These did not constitute a separate item until it was separated from university physics research facilities in 1963 but did receive grants before that date. One of the earliest was $500,000 in 1956 to the Massachusetts Institute of Technology for assistance in constructing a nuclear reactor. In 1966, there were forty-five grants, totaling $1,175,000 for engineering research facilities.

Social science research facilities. These received seven grants totaling $771,200 in 1966. Such a facility was defined in the Foundation's report for 1964 as, "a national or regional research resource which is unique, or rarely duplicated, in purpose, design, or location. Typically it involves active participation by scientists from a number of universities, with the intent that ultimately it will be available for use by qualified scientists from all parts of the country."

This program aids independent nonprofit research organizations, as well as university-affiliated organizations that function as suppliers of extraordinary data or data services.

Support has been furnished, for example, to a laboratory for research in the archaeology of the Near East, to a field station in Yucatan for anthropologists and social psychologists, and to facilities for storing and handling data collections for use in social science research.

OCEANOGRAPHY

In several instances, a big science project is not handled as a unit in any one of the four program activities described in the preceding sections of this chapter. Oceanography is one, although not the only, example.

Oceanography, or marine sciences, as it is often called, is not an entity or discipline, like physics or engineering. It is based on a physical location—the ocean—and a scientific study of it involves many disciplines, including mathematics, physics, chemistry, and biology. The Foundation supports research, facilities, and educational programs in oceanographic institutions on shore and on research vessels at sea. Support is provided for scientific research projects, ship construction and conversion, construction or renovation of laboratory buildings, docks, and similar facilities, provision of operating costs for ships, training programs, special courses and conferences, and maintenance of sorting centers and data centers.

The National Science Foundation and the Office of Naval Research each provide support for about 40 per cent of the basic research in oceanography conducted at universities and colleges, and the remaining 20 per cent is expended in a number of federal agencies. Total oceanographic obligations of the Foundation in fiscal year 1966 were over $46 million; estimated obligations for 1967 were $26 million and for 1968, $33.6 million. (The decrease in amounts is due largely to the termination of Project Mohole.) They were divided as follows:

Basic research project support	$17,228,870
Specialized research facilities	2,730,718
National research programs	26,432,467
Total	$46,032,055

The National Sea Grant College and Program Act of 1966 assigned a new program to the Foundation, for which Congress permitted expenditures of $1 million for fiscal year 1967. This program is administered by the newly established Office of Sea Grant Programs, and under it, universities and existing oceanographic research centers such as Woods Hole in Massachusetts and Scripps Institution in California are eligible for grants in three major areas—research, marine advisory programs, and training of personnel. The office coordinates its efforts with other federal agencies working in oceanography.

APPLIED RESEARCH

A great deal of effort has been expended in trying to define *basic* research and *applied* research in specific language, for the practical purpose of allocating projects to one or the other category. Such a definition as a basis for allocating projects is a necessity since the Foundation's authority to make grants is for basic scientific research only (Section 1862(a)(2), and it must be certain that requests for grants are not ineligible because they are for applied rather than for basic research. The project research grants awarded to institutions for the work of individual scientists or small groups of scientists working together, the national research programs, the national research centers, and the grants to institutions for specialized research facilities and equipment are the major basic research programs of the Foundation, but many of their other programs contribute importantly to the conduct of basic research.

The general difference between basic and applied research is not difficult to define, however difficult it may turn out to be to classify particular examples. Basic research is devoted primarily to the discovery of new facts about nature and to finding, testing, and developing general principles. The discovery of radioactivity is an example of the discovery of a new fact, and the statement and verification of the law of gravity is an example of a general scientific principle. The results of basic research are used by applied scientists, inventors, and engineers in many practical ways. For example, the American electronics industry uses the discovery of the electron and its applications, and this basic science came out of the physicist's attempt to understand the nature of matter. Almost every one of the annual reports of the Foundation has contained discussion of the nature of basic science and the importance of supporting it as a public service.

Within the last few years, considerable emphasis has been placed on the need for increasing support for applied science, not as an alternative to support for basic science but as an additional program. In the second session of the Eighty-ninth

Congress (1966) and in both sessions of the Ninetieth (1967 and 1968), consideration was given to a measure amending the National Science Foundation Act of 1950 in several ways. (For a description of this bill, which became Public Law 90-407, and its legislative history see Chapter XII.)

One new provision authorized initiation of "scientific research, including applied research," at academic and other nonprofit institutions. When so directed by the President, the Foundation may also support through other appropriate organizations, applied scientific research relevant to national problems involving the public interest.

House Report 1650 (1966) of the House Committee on Science and Astronautics included a statement supporting this new section:

> Support for applied research is authorized, but is made permissive and is at the discretion of the Director. It must be borne in mind that NSF was established to further basic, or fundamental, research, and it is not the intent of this legislation to change that element of the Foundation's character. NSF should and must retain its central mission of fostering basis research in science and engineering; the authority to engage in support of applied research should not be used at the expense of the basic.
>
> Nonetheless, there are important occasions when Foundation backing for applied research appears warranted. These include, but are not limited to, research necessary for the solution of major national problems involving the public interest and the furthering of engineering research into early phases of application, after which other groups may take over the hard facets of applied research and development.

All witnesses appearing at the hearings approved this provision, although some expressed doubts about it. Some felt that if a very large and expensive applied research grant were included in the Foundation's budget, other parts of the program might be starved in order to keep the total appropriation within limits Congress might establish. Also, it was argued that the support of applied research at colleges and universities might be "the thin edge of the wedge," which could ultimately result in pressures to support mission-oriented work at the expense of basic research, with damaging effects on science, the academic institutions, and, in the long run, on our economic well-being.

The director's statement in the Foundation's annual report for 1966 contained a strong statement of approval of the proposal authorizing the Foundation to support applied research as defined in the new legislation. He wrote that it is an appropriate concern regarding science that its fruits be utilized to the maximum extent. He continued:

> To make satisfactory progress, it is essential that science and technology be in appropriate balance and of reciprocal benefit to each other. New knowledge developed from basic research should be used fully in the shortest time possible to benefit mankind. Conversely, new developments in applied science and technology have a great deal to contribute to basic research by providing insights into better instrumentation, improved methodology, and new areas of exploration. As the one agency of the Federal Government dedicated to the health and welfare of science as a whole, the National Science Foundation has an important role to play in this interface—in helping to link progress in basic research to the goals and concerns of applied science and technology, and vice versa. Within this context the authority to support applied research, especially in the universities, would, in my opinion, provide a significant addition to the Foundation's powers.

PATENTS

The policies and practices of the Foundation with respect to patents arising out of research supported by Foundation grants are, of course, closely related to the very complicated policies and practices of many other federal agencies, the universities and foundations, and business corporations. The U.S. government, representing the public, has the obligation to insure both that the holder of a patent shall be able to enjoy legitimate benefits, and that the public shall receive the use of valuable developments. Reconciliation of these interests, which frequently diverge very widely, has been and still is a difficult matter.

The Constitution of the United States grants to Congress the power "to promote the progress of science and useful arts, by securing for limited times to authors and inventors the exclusive right to their respective writings and discoveries." Under this authority, Congress enacted the first patent law and the first copyright law in 1790. Although the patent system is almost as old as the United States itself and its basic principles have not been changed in the past hundred years, the increasing demands made on it, particularly in the last decades, have made it less satisfactory in many important respects.

Many of the problems in present patent administration do not specifically affect the Foundation since they relate to patents arising from government-industry contracts, rather than from grants for research. Vannevar Bush stated in *Science—The Endless Frontier* the patent policies he thought should be adopted by the science agency he was proposing. He believed that the Foundation should set up its own general rules, interfering as little as possible with the practices of the different universities and research institutions. He predicted that obtaining of patents by universities on work financed by the Foundation would remain a minor byproduct of the fundamental research undertaken. In cooperating with organizations outside the government, he wrote:

> The public interest will normally be adequately protected if the Government receives a royalty-free license for governmental purposes under any patents resulting from work financed by the Foundation. There should be no obligation on the research institution to patent discoveries made as a result of support from the Foundation. There should certainly *not* be any absolute requirement that all rights in such discoveries be assigned to the Government, but it should be left to the discretion of the director and the interested Division whether in special cases the public interest requires such an assignment. Legislation on this point should leave to the Members of the Foundation discretion as to

its patent policy in order that patent arrangements may be adjusted as circumstances and the public interest require.

The present law covering the National Science Foundation's authority concerning patents provides that the Foundation's contracts or other arrangements for the conduct of scientific research shall contain provisions governing patent rights that will insure both the public and the inventor's interests. Officers and employees of the Foundation may not acquire rights to any invention produced in connection with official duties or related to the subject matter of such duties.

Each annual report of the Foundation from 1960 to the present has briefly described the patents issued resulting from scientific activities supported by the Foundation. With certain noted exceptions, the Foundation has secured for the federal government royalty-free licenses, to utilize these inventions for government purposes, as stipulated in the provisions of the grant and fellowship awards involved. The first patents were issued in 1960, when there were two, followed by four in 1961, four in 1962, two in 1963, four in 1964, one in 1965, and five in 1966—a total of twenty-two.

With such a small number of examples, few conclusions can be drawn, but it may be noted that only one patent was issued to the United States and only one to a person working under an individual grant, that most of the patents were for inventions in physics and chemistry, and that most were issued under grants to smaller universities. There was no evidence of a progressive increase in the number of issuances per year in the 1960–66 period.

Important patent legislation has been considered but not enacted by the Congress in recent sessions. The bills have not specifically related to the National Science Foundation, but have dealt with the establishment of uniform national policy concerning property rights resulting from government contracts with industry, rather than with the type of grant to support independent research that the Foundation makes to a university or an individual. However, the various arguments concerning patent rights arising from federal contracts with industrial firms are almost identical with those concerning patent rights arising from federal grants.

An excellent presentation of the subject of patent rights was included in House Report 1942 (1964), one of the studies published by the Select Committee on Government Research of the House of Representatives. It described the different kinds of policies followed by various government agencies with respect to titles developed under federal research and development contracts. The Department of Defense, the National Science Foundation, the National Bureau of Standards, the Weather Bureau, and the General Services Administration permit the contractor to retain patent rights, with the government receiving a royalty-free license. The Atomic Energy Commission, the National Aeronautics and Space Administration, the Department of Agriculture, the Department of the Interior, and the Housing and Home Finance Agency take title to inventions developed under their contracts. The report set forth the opposing arguments for a uniform title policy, for a uniform license policy, and against an absolute policy.

VI

Science Education Activities

James B. Conant, the first chairman of the National Science Board, wrote the Foreword for the first report of the National Science Foundation (1950–51). In it, he expressed this judgment concerning support of science education activities:

> In the advance of science and its application to many practical problems, there is no substitute for first-class men. Ten second-rate scientists or engineers cannot do the work of one who is in the first rank. Therefore, if the aims of Congress as set forth in the National Science Foundation Act are to be fulfilled, there must be all over the United States intensive effort to discover latent scientific talent and provide for its adequate development. This means strengthening many institutions which have not yet developed their full potentialities as scientific centers, it means assisting promising young men and women who have completed their college education but require postgraduate training in order to become leaders in science and engineering. To this end a fellowship program has been placed high on the list of priorities by the National Science Board. Again, given time, the expenditure of public funds in this enterprise, I feel certain, will prove to have been a most advantageous investment by the American people.

This brief statement of intent was immediately carried into effect by the Foundation. By April, 1952, the Foundation had awarded 624 graduate fellowships in the sciences for the coming academic year. The students who received these awards had been selected from more than 3,000 applicants from all parts of the United States, its territories and possessions, and from among American citizens abroad. The selections had been made solely on the basis of ability, although in cases of substantially equal ability geographical distribution had been considered. The pattern of distribution included a large number of awards to graduating college seniors entering their first year of graduate work (in contrast with the policy of previous federal fellowship programs), with lesser numbers to second year and to postgraduate students. In order of number of awards, the biological sciences ranked first, with chemistry, physics, engineering, mathematics, earth sciences, agriculture, astronomy, and anthropology, in that order.

Originally, the Foundation's support for education in the sciences was furnished only in the form of awards of graduate fellowships to graduate students and advanced scholars of unusual ability. Very soon, when it was realized that improvement and stimulation of science education at all levels must be added to support of graduate education, comprehensive support for science education was initiated. To carry out this policy, as early as 1953, the Foundation supported teacher institutes, and other programs were added and expanded. At the present time, the many science education activities of the Foundation may be described under these headings:

Graduate Education in Science
    Graduate Fellowships and Traineeships
    Fellowships for Advanced Scholars in Science
    Advanced Science Education Activities
Undergraduate Education in Science
    Defining the Need
    Undergraduate Research Participation
    College Teacher Programs
    Instructional Improvement
    Special Projects for Undergraduate Education
Pre-College Education in Science
    Improvement of Instructional Materials
    Cooperation in School System Improvement
    Activities for High School Students

Pre-College Teacher Education Activities
Pre-Service Teacher Training

LEGAL AUTHORITY

The following provisions under section 1862 of the National Science Foundation Act of 1950 relate to education activities:

A. The Foundation is authorized and directed

1. to develop and encourage the pursuit of a national policy for the promotion of basic research and education in the sciences:

2. to initiate and support basic scientific research and programs to strengthen scientific research potential in the mathematical, physical, medical, biological, engineering, and other sciences, by making contracts or other arrangements (including grants, loans, and other forms of assistance) to support such scientific activities, and to appraise the impact of research upon industrial development and upon the general welfare.

. . .

4. to award, as provided in section 1869 of this title, scholarships and graduate fellowships in the mathematical, physical, medical, biological, engineering, and other sciences.

. . .

B. In exercising the authority and discharging the functions referred to in subsection (a) of this section, it shall be one of the objectives of the Foundation to strengthen basic research and education in the sciences, including independent research by individuals, throughout the United States, including its territories and possessions, and to avoid undue concentration of such research and education.

Executive Order 10521 (March 17, 1954) added to section 1862 the provision that the Foundation in consultation with educational institutions, the heads of federal agencies, and the Commissioner of Education, shall study the effects of the federal grants and contracts for scientific research and development upon educational institutions, and shall recommend policies and procedures for the conduct of such programs.

Section 1869, on scholarships and graduate fellowships, provided that these awards for scientific study or work are to be used at appropriate nonprofit American or foreign institutions selected by the recipients. Citizens or nationals of the United States are eligible. They are to be selected solely on the basis of ability, although if two applicants are of substantially equal ability and there are not enough scholarships or fellowships to award one to each, the award shall be made in such a manner that it will result in a wide distribution of grants on a geographical basis. The Foundation may refuse or revoke an award if the Board judges that it is not in the best interests of the United States.

Section 1873(g), on utilization of appropriations in making contracts, provided that the Foundation, in making contracts or other arrangements for scientific research will attempt to achieve these objectives: (1) having the work performed by qualified organizations, agencies and institutions, or individuals; (2) strengthening the research staff of organizations; (3) aiding institutions, agencies, or organizations that, if aided, will advance basic research; and (4) encouraging independent basic research by individuals.

FINANCES

Considering that the Foundation had a total appropriation of only $225,000 for its first year, the fact that its expenditures for education activities were only $11,400 is not surprising.

As time went on, special programs were added, and there was a steady increase in the amounts of expenditures, until by 1966 they had grown more than ten thousand times.

Table 10 presents a summary, by category of support, of actual expenditures in this field for fiscal year 1966.

It is important to remember that the amount spent by the Foundation on support of science education is by no means all of the NSF funds going to colleges and universities. Estimates are that $450 million of the $500 million total for fiscal year 1966 were expended in the institutions of higher learning. This amount covered the basic research projects of faculty members, the operation of four national research centers

TABLE 10
Expenditures for Education Activities, 1966

Activity	Amount Spent
Science education support	
Precollege	
Improvement of quality of institutional programs	
Course content improvement	$9,916,681
Cooperative college-school program	1,957,426
Special projects	0
Improvement of quality and competence of instructional staff and students	
Supplemental training for teachers	
Institutes	36,634,363
Research participation	719,237
Supplemental project	882,361
Science education for students	1,972,500
Subtotal	52,082,568
Undergraduate education in science	
Improvement of quality of instructional programs	
Course content improvement	5,647,271
Instructional equipment for undergraduate education	7,736,045
Improvement of quality and competence of instructional staff and students	
Supplemental training for teachers	
Institutes	3,896,237
Research participation	1,381,023
Science education for students	6,582,865
Special projects	1,406,327
Subtotal	26,649,768
Graduate education in science	
Fellowships and traineeships	44,484,949
Special graduate science education projects	
Advanced science seminar projects	1,087,940
Subtotal	45,572,889
TOTAL	$124,305,225

by university associates, and the support and operation of research facilities and equipment. These three activities make up about half of the NSF budget. Many of the grants for graduate student support go to the universities; the holder of an NSF fellowship or traineeship spends much of his grant in payment to the university; and the universities themselves receive amounts for awards to graduate students.

A comparison of the NSF expenditures for science education activities with the total of all government-sponsored university research indicates that the Foundation's expenditures are about 12 per cent of the total. The Foundation's support of basic research is about 8 per cent of the government's total expenditures for this purpose.

A recent report, prepared by the Foundation for the Office of Science and Technology, contained information about the relative amounts of support for science education by the different government agencies based on actual data for fiscal year 1965. It showed that federal obligations for the support of academic science and other educational activities in universities and colleges were $2.3 billion in that year. Three-fourths of this amount was allocated to academic science—47 per cent for research and development, 6 per cent for research and development facilities, and 23 per cent for other academic-science activities. The remaining 24 per cent was obligated for other educational activities. The Department of Health, Education, and Welfare was the largest contributor of support for academic science (primarily through the programs of the National Institutes of Health), the National Science Foundation was second, and the Department of Defense was third.

The Foundation's original program of aid to students at the graduate level through fellowships and traineeships, between 1956 and 1966 cost more than $210 million. In that period, more than 42,000 fellowships had been granted to 151,000 applicants, and 8,137 traineeships had been granted to 193 institutions for them to award. The Foundation's annual publication of grants and awards for fiscal year 1966 contained eighty pages of lists, under seventeen different headings, for the vastly extended science education programs.

GRADUATE EDUCATION IN SCIENCE

Science education and scientific research at the graduate level are closely intertwined, and the leading educational institutions are, at the same time, outstanding centers of academic research. The process by which a graduate student advances toward his doctoral degree illustrates this relationship, and postdoctoral programs show an even more intimate relationship. NSF research project grant funds go directly to support educationally valuable research activities of graduate students.

In 1966, the Foundation spent nearly $45 million on eight fellowship and traineeship programs: graduate fellowships, cooperative graduate fellowships, summer fellowships for graduate teaching assistants, graduate traineeships, postdoctoral fellowships, senior postdoctoral fellowships, science faculty fellowships, and senior foreign scientist fellowships.

An NSF "fellowship" is awarded by the Foundation in national competition on the basis of the candidate's merit and ability, without assignment of quotas by scientific field or discipline. In 1966, the Foundation made 702 fellowship awards.

A "traineeship" is granted by the college or university itself. The Foundation places emphasis on making grants under this program to those institutions where existing facilities and staff can accommodate additional first-year students in programs of high quality. In recent years, predoctoral students have received the largest number of fellowships and traineeships.

The four types of fellowships for advanced scholars in science are senior postdoctoral, postdoctoral, science faculty, and senior foreign scientist. The last-named fellowship program has resulted in so many requests that the number of participating institutions was increased from eighty to two hundred. Distinguished scientists from other countries conduct seminars, participate in research, and lecture in American universities.

Funds for advanced science education activities allow for flexibility in assisting the universities to adjust to the rapid changes in educational demand at the graduate level. Thirty-eight advanced science seminars were financed in 1966. Special projects were supported to help the institutions to expand and alter their existing departments to improve their quality. Increasing the public understanding of science, which admittedly is less than might be desired, is a relatively new activity of the Foundation, and most of its efforts are exploratory projects aimed at identifying devices and techniques that will increase the layman's understanding of science and its role. Seminars and conferences have been held by universities for science writers, editors, and others connected with the mass media. Science film series have been produced. Two graduate-degree programs designed to produce science communicators have been supported.

UNDERGRADUATE EDUCATION IN SCIENCE

Today, there are about 3 million people employed in science and technology. By 1970, it is estimated that there will be 4 million. These million new people, and replacements for many of the present 3 million personnel, must be furnished in large part from the graduate schools of the universities. But graduate students are obtained from the undergraduate institutions, and many persons engaged in scientific and technological occupations have only undergraduate training. The undergraduate institutions face a tremendous task in meeting this demand, and they are encountering serious problems in recruiting and retaining well-trained teachers, modernizing their courses and equipment, and providing special courses for youths of unusually high aptitude.

The Foundation has tried in many ways to define these needs and to devise means of meeting them. National and regional curriculum conferences, and surveys of equipment needs made by a number of scientific societies are examples of such efforts. The Foundation has stated that the "continuing dialog between staff and teaching scientists" remains one of its "most effective mechanisms for monitoring academic science needs."

A program for undergraduate research participation has been in effect since 1960, and it has provided students of high ability the opportunity to work as junior colleagues under the guidance of competent research advisers or to engage in independent study activities. Such an opportunity is excellent preparation for graduate work.

College teachers who were originally well prepared but who now need refresher courses, others who never were adequately prepared, and still others who are assigned college teaching in subspecialties of their major fields in which they are not fully qualified also are provided interesting opportunities. Teacher institutes (academic year, summer, and in-service institutes) and conferences, and opportunities for research participation are the activities currently made available to them through NSF support. In 1966, 358 grants were made, involving 3,721 participants, at a cost of $5.28 million. The titles of the various institutes and conferences are largely self-explanatory. They offer different types of programs, to a considerable extent based on the time which teachers have available. Academic year institutes are for teachers who are on full-time leave, while summer and in-service institutes and conferences make it possible for the teacher to work full time while using nonteaching time for course work.

But improvement in the abilities of undergraduate college teachers is only half of the story. The other half is improvement in undergraduate instructional programs. Science curriculum improvement involves innovation and experimentation, and the Foundation has been able to develop a group of scientists who have devoted substantial effort to the solution of the educational problems of their disciplines. The Union of Social Science Teaching was organized in 1966, and there have been national college commissions in biology, chemistry, physics, geology, engineering, mathematics, geography, and agriculture. Course outlines and many kinds of teaching materials are developed, with the particular advantage of being highly current.

Provision of special equipment for science teaching supplements teacher training and course improvement, and the colleges, through matching federal funds, have quickly availed themselves of this kind of assistance. Since 1962, the Foundation has awarded some $37 million to 957 institutions for the purchase of instructional equipment.

The Foundation also supports promising experimental projects to develop and test new ideas in undergraduate science education. Often, these serve as pilot models for application on a broad scale. Among many examples are inter-institutional associations enabling colleges and universities to pool their instructional resources, state, regional, or national curriculum conferences, and visiting-scientist projects to aid the instructional programs.

PRECOLLEGE EDUCATION IN SCIENCE

If college students are to be encouraged to undertake scientific courses in college, their experiences in the primary and secondary school systems must prepare them adequately and motivate them to take such courses. To this end, the Foundation supports several types of assistance to precollege science education, much as it supports graduate and undergraduate education.

As early as 1954, the Foundation began to enlist the active collaboration of leading scientists and teachers and other experts in carrying out course content improvement efforts. At first, most of the effort was spent on development of materials at the high school level, but at present there are many major projects for elementary and junior high schools. By the end of 1966, more than 275 definitive editions of textbooks and other printed materials had been developed, and many of them were available through commercial publishers. More than 500 separate scientific topics were available in films for classroom use.

The local school system is the agency with ultimate responsibility for carrying out curricular reform in the classroom. Local school boards and school superintendents must understand the requirements imposed by improved curricula, and competence of the classroom teachers is essential to success in the adoption of new materials.

The Foundation supports the Cooperative College-School Science Program, which provides collaborative efforts between school systems and neighboring colleges or universities. Fifty-seven projects at fifty institutions were in operation by 1966. Two examples were the physics teaching program in the state of Missouri and an elementary school mathematics program in large urban school systems.

Direct aid to high school students is furnished through the Secondary Science Training Program, which provides challenging classroom work or research participation for very talented high school students interested in science, mathematics, or engineering. In 1966, nearly 6,000 students in 109 schools received grants. Special summer courses for high-ability high school students have been extremely successful.

Because the National Science Foundation considers that ensuring the competence of teachers is a matter of primary concern, it has supported teacher-training institutes and other teacher activities benefiting about half of the secondary school science teachers and a very small number of key elementary school teachers. In 1966, approximately 43,400 secondary school teachers were offered study and training opportunities in 850 projects sponsored by the NSF—about 20 per cent of the science and mathematics teachers in grades 7 through 12. For secondary school teachers, the activities included academic year institutes, summer institutes and conferences, inservice institutes, research participation, and special projects. For elementary school personnel, there were summer and inservice institutes.

The supply of qualified teachers of science and mathematics is admittedly inadequate. One solution to this problem—refresher or advanced training for mature individuals who are changing careers with the intent to become teachers—has strong Foundation support. Retired Armed Services personnel and housewives, for example, are participating in such projects. In 1966, seven grants, totaling $156,805, were awarded for preservice teacher training. The Foundation also sponsors special projects to improve the training of persons who themselves train teachers.

ADMINISTRATION OF RESEARCH GRANTS AND CONTRACTS

Despite the steady increase in the amount of federal support for science education grants and projects and the widespread approval of them, the titles of three articles, published in June and July of 1967, reflected growing concern over some built-in difficulties. They were: "Mounting an Attack on Research Red-Tape," *Scientific Research,* Vol. 2 (June, 1967), pp. 35–38; "Federal Paper-Work Explosion: New Form Bothers Universities," *Science,* Vol. 156 (June 16, 1967), pp. 1468–69; "The Administration of Federal Aid: A Monstrosity Has Been Created," *Science,* Vol. 157 (July 7, 1967), pp. 43–47.

The obvious conclusion that a more complicated situation than is generally appreciated had by this time developed is an understatement. So many reports, studies, and articles dealing with the troubles attendant on federal support to education in general and to science education specifically, have appeared as the amounts of federal funds and the numbers of participants have increased, that it is possible only to indicate the major problems which have arisen, and still persist.

In 1964, the Select Committee on Government Research of the House of Representatives published a series of studies, numbers one and seven of which dealt, respectively, with the administration of research and development grants, and with contract policies and procedures for research and development. These contained descriptions of the two types of support and indicated the principal difficulties involved in their administration. Simply to list the procedural steps for both types demonstrates the complexity of the processes and offers clues as to the opportunities for administrative tangles and differences of opinion between the federal agency making the grant, or entering into the contract, and the university as the other party:

Steps in grant procedures
Initiation of projects

Initial review and recommendation of project proposals
Final review and agency decision
In-progress review of grant projects
Procedure at end of grant
Steps in contract procedures
  Handling of contracting
  Issuance of regulations
  Selection of projects
  Selection of contractors
  Handling of variations
  Amendments and extensions
  Termination procedure
  Control of projects
  Supervision of contracts

The terms "grant" and "contract" should perhaps be clarified. Grants are used to support research that is largely basic in character and is conducted principally in institutions of higher learning. They are free from the numerous procurement requirements applying to contracts and do not include the wordy clauses and conditions common to government contracts. Contracts may be used to support basic research, but they may also be used to sponsor and finance developmental and other activity in the field of science and technology not eligible for grants. In general, grants may not be made to industrial organizations, and contracts are usually used to support and sponsor research and development in industry. The Select Committee estimated that, in the 1963–64 period, approximately 10 per cent of the federal government's research and development budget was spent extramurally for basic research and that grants and contracts each accounted for approximately one-half of that amount. In addition, they estimated that private industry performs (almost exclusively through contracts) more than 75 per cent of the dollar value of the government's research and development program.

The federal departments and agencies performing or supporting research and development operate under many different provisions of statutes and regulations, and consequently there is no standardization in their grants' and contracts' policies and procedures. Many common provisions and practices exist, along with very marked differences. This situation explains in large part the impossibility of formulating a clear statement of what could be called "federal policies and procedures," and it also explains many of the criticisms which are made, both by the federal agencies and the universities viewing the situation from the standpoints of their particular interests.

One basic problem underlies all the criticisms. The federal government (meaning the Congress, the Executive Office of the President—particularly the Bureau of the Budget, the Federal Council on Science and Technology, the Science Adviser to the President, and the Office of Science and Technology—and the twenty or so departments and agencies supporting federal research and development through grants and contracts) expends constantly increasing amounts of public funds for research and development. It is their duty to determine wise policies, to plan adequate and suitable programs, to determine the distribution of funds to institutions and individuals, to institute proper procedures, and to exercise sufficient control or review to insure that the expenditures are made legally and honestly by the recipients. There can be no objection to their exercise of this duty. The implementation is another story, and that is where the problems begin.

The colleges and universities, their faculty members, and members and representatives of the science community have an equally strong position, based on two widely accepted principles: the federal government should not control academic institutions: research (particularly basic research) cannot operate under any kind of external controls. They hold that academic freedom and unfettered research are not to be protected primarily for teachers and researchers as individuals, but in the public interest. Like the position of the government, the position of the academic and scientific representatives, is unassailable. Again, it is in the implementation that problems arise.

The scientists' insistence on independence and freedom and the government's insistence on careful distribution and accountability for public funds have not been reconciled. Possibly they never can be, and the best we can hope for is a compromise only partially satisfactory to the two interests. But efforts are being made to effect a reconciliation. Somewhere between the extremes of strict and minute federal controls and unlimited academic and scientific freedom many responsible persons from both sides feel, there must be a point of reasonable, workable agreement.

A single short paragraph from a 1964 report by the Committee on Science and Public Policy of the National Academy of Sciences summarized this subject:

One principle dominates all others in the present report: The government and the universities must work within two noble traditions characteristic of all free societies—the political freedom of a democratic people and the freedom of scientific inquiry. The scientific community, the Congress, and the Executive have long since agreed both that a strong and free development of science is a national necessity and that accountability for the use of government funds is a fundamental part of the exchange by which a people in a democracy entrusts power to its leaders, who are in fact and theory public servants. Can freedom of scientific inquiry and accountability be reconciled? We believe that they can be and must be. We ask in this report: What are the policies by which accountable support can effectively advance scientific inquiry in the common interest? How can inaccurate conceptions of both the *necessary freedom for scientific research and the accountability of funds* be prevented from stifling the fruits of research—a potent resource of our society not only for today but for the future?

Of all the problems, those arising from indirect costs, cost-sharing, and effort-reporting are the most intractable. In arriving at the conditions under which a grant will be made, the government agency and the recipient of the grant have to determine the amounts of indirect costs involved in the project and agree on the relative amounts of the cost of administering the grant which will be borne by each of the two parties. The cost-sharing process is almost unbelievably difficult, and it has become a center of emotional reactions from all sources involved in it. Congressional committees, the Bureau of the Budget, the Committee on Academic Science and Engineering (CASE) of the Federal Council on Science and Technology, professional organizations of professors and scientists, and the federal agencies all participate vigorously in the controversy. New formulas, devised to resolve disagreement seem to arouse more discontent.

In *Science* (July 7, 1967), D. S. Greenberg, reporting on a survey of eighty-one colleges and universities receiving 65 per cent of all federal expenditures in institutions of higher learning, came to this unhappy conclusion:

. . . after allowance is made for the fact that government has an instinct for tidiness and accountability while universities are untidy and often unaccountable, it appears that the administrative system between government and academe is en route to chaos. It is difficult to find broad agreement on remedies, but remedies are badly needed. They are not likely to take effect if they emanate from any of the lower-level committees that toy with these matters in the federal executive hierarchy. The incredible confusion and ill-will generated by the cost-sharing regulations are a monument to the efficacy of these committees. Perhaps it is time for the White House or Congress to decree that coherent, rational, and predictable government-wide regulations on the use of federal funds for academic research and higher education are necessary and attainable. And then let the quest for administrative sanity start from that point.

The arrangements for the amount and the kind of reporting to which recipients should be subject are possibly slightly less controversial but still constitute a problem seemingly far from a satisfactory solution. Apparently, asking a college professor or a scientist to make fairly detailed and frequent reports arouses automatic and vigorous opposition. But congressional committees persist in asking the Foundation and other government agencies what is being accomplished for the millions of dollars in expenditures and are frequently highly critical of the occasional inability of these agencies to give an accounting —an accounting, of course, possible only if an adequate reporting system is in operation.

For a time after the Soviet Union launched Sputnik I, Congress—and almost every one else—succumbed automatically to any proposal that was tagged "science" or "research," and few questions were asked before large appropriations were made. Ten years later, those "good old days" had gone, probably forever. Only appropriations for health research arouse such enthusiasm in Congress that the National Institutes of Health receive not only whatever they request, but frequently are presented with more than they ask for by a Congress seldom so generous. Congress now has many members and many committee staffs who are very well acquainted with the details of the various agencies' budgets and operations. With the claims of urgent domestic problems and of the war in Vietnam, with a rising federal debt, science and research have real competition for the federal dollar.

The Impact of NSF Science Activities on the Schools

There are so many general and special federal education activities becoming effective at the same time in the educational institutions, at all levels from prekindergarten to postdoctoral, that trying to identify which program is producing which effect is egg-unscrambling in an extreme form. In Chapter XI of this book, the relationships of the NSF science activities to those of other agencies of the federal government are described in some detail. The following discussion emphasizes the impact of the Foundation's activities on educational institutions insofar as they can be identified separately.

Study Number VI (1964) of the Select Committee, cited earlier, reported that about 90 per cent of federal research funds available to universities were contributed by the Department of Health, Education, and Welfare, the Department of Defense, the Atomic Energy Commission, and the National Aeronautics and Space Administration. Of the remaining 10 per cent, the NSF contributed approximately 7 per cent. The study also showed that the large proportion of all funds was expended by the top one hundred universities in the country. Since its publication, effort has been made to increase the funds, both absolutely and relatively, available to the universities and colleges smaller than those listed as having received the bulk of support at earlier dates.

The Select Committee dealt with "questions of balance" and noted that the effects of the federal government's heavy support of the natural sciences, its small support of the social sciences, and its even smaller support of the humanities have undoubtedly produced academic problems. Permanent distortion in the faculty, the curriculum, and the career planning of students may have been produced. The relationships between research and teaching have changed markedly since the greatly increased amounts of federal support for research conducted by university faculty have been available. Particularly questionable has been the effect on the teaching of undergraduates, because graduate instruction and research are widely believed to compete with undergraduate teaching for the time and attention of the faculty, to the detriment of the undergraduate. Eminent university educators have emphatically denied that this is true and have insisted that the goal of the university is to encourage both activities in proper proportions. "This balance," the committee said, "will not be found by any external power, or fixed by rigid rules. It must, and the committee is confident it will, be achieved by each university."

In its appraisal of the basic system the committee approved the systems of project and institutional grants of the federal government, both of which methods are used by the National Science Foundation, and stated:

. . . the benefits to the Federal Government from its practice of supporting research in the universities (and that being mainly basic research), are almost incalculable. By the same token, the benefits accruing to the universities from this practice and relationship are likewise very great. Witness after witness who appeared before the committee confirmed that whatever rank of competence their institutions enjoy, especially in the sciences, this results to a large degree from Federal support.

Among the study's summary recommendations, the following were especially relevant:

Believing that it is of crucial importance that additional centers of educational and scientific excellence be developed, the committee recommends the careful but sure expansion of the science development program of the National Science Foundation, which may help to boost potentially excellent institutions to first-rank status; ultimately, such a program will undoubtedly contribute to the geographical broadening of our scientific capabilities.

The committee reiterates the recommendations it made in its study on grants for the strengthening of the project grant as a most desirable way to "purchase" basic research and to exploit the excellent capabilities of particular researchers.

The institutional grant system is an efficient complement to the project system, especially where broad agency missions are involved; it also contributes to the building up of superior research capabilities in institutions. The committee recommends its continuance.

THE PROBLEM OF FEDERAL CONTROL

A really serious question arises with the realization that a large proportion of the National Science Foundation's funds goes to the educational institutions of the country. When the Foundation was first proposed, many people feared that it would result in federal control of the educational system. During the past decade, as we have seen, the Foundation has been spending much effort on improvement of secondary schools and of high school teaching—retraining teachers and developing curricula in physics, mathematics, biology, and chemistry, for example. Hundreds of thousands of pupils from kindergarten through the senior year of high school have studied one or more of the new courses, under teachers who have received training in the NSF programs. This is exactly the kind of development that was feared when such activities were initiated. Yet little objection has been raised to these programs. The primary and secondary school systems are participating in them, in increasing numbers, with enthusiasm.

As might be expected, there is today a great difference of opinion as to the over-all impact of the Foundation's science education activities.

The House Committee on Science and Astronautics, in its 1965 and 1966 studies by the Subcommittee on Science, Research, and Development, identified several weaknesses as follows:

> NSF support for graduate training of engineering students does not seem proportionate to anticipated national needs. NSF's curriculum research and development has yet to extend undergraduate science education, especially for the smaller liberal arts colleges. NSF science teacher training does not provide opportunities to scientists and engineers interested in teaching as a second career. Also, while it is not the job of the Foundation to refresh the education of working scientists and engineers, it would seem that the NSF's educational research should extend to the problems of personal obsolescence of professional personnel caused by rapid changes of science and technology. Also, because the results of education are less readily discernible than the results of basic research, there is needed a mechanism, which does not now exist, to evelute the effectiveness of the Foundation's educational programs.
>   . . . however, the impact of NSF educational programs is much more a function of appropriations than it is of the means for distributing the funds. The main thing to be considered is the sufficiency of present and future finding.

In an article in *International Science and Technology* (April, 1966), David Allison evaluated the work of the Foundation in its first sixteen years. He wrote that the Congress of today views the Foundation as a permanent part of the governmental establishment, that it considers support of science, including science education, as a national commitment—and that that is a drastic change. He continued, describing "the programs in science education, programs involving the improvement of grammar school and high school teaching," and said, "Currently, the Foundation spends about $60 million per year in this area, most of it for the retraining of teachers."

Then he summarized:

> . . . if we make a judgment on the basis of numbers of students being taught, we must conclude that the Foundation is having a significant influence on the nation's educational system. And we would have to say that this is a well-conceived and thoughtfully planned campaign, for it involves more than simply the introduction of new textbooks into the classroom; it also involves the training of teachers to levels where they will be capable of handling the new material.

But the Foundation is not able to exercise control over teaching. Indeed, the Foundation can neither exercise control over the teaching of science nor over the doing of science. What limits its power?

The limitation is the Foundation's philosophy. The Foundation does not initiate. It reacts to the initiations of outsiders, and it reacts by providing money, or by refusing to provide money. Further, "the Foundation" is not Director Leland Haworth, nor the 300 professional people—most of them people with scientific backgrounds—who make up his staff. Practically speaking, the Foundation is Haworth, his staff, plus the 24 members of the National Science Board, plus some 39 advisory panels, divisional committees, councils, advisory committees, and so on, which are made up of several hundred scientists and engineers who represent various technical fields and who come to the Foundation periodically to advise on new programs and to evaluate the proposals that have been submitted by *other* scientists and engineers.

VII

Institutional Support for Science

The belief that the science programs of the universities and colleges must be strengthened through what is now referred to as "institutional support" is by no means a product of the recent years during which such support programs have been instituted and have developed very rapidly.

The Foundation has always recognized the validity of this principle. In its first annual report, there was comment on the fact that the benefits of federal grants and contracts had tended to be concentrated in a relatively few institutions. The report stated:

> The National Science Foundation proposes to support basic research on as broad a geographic and institutional basis as possible. In the small institutions, many of which are operating on meager budgets, relatively small sums of money may make it possible to retain the services of an unusually competent research investigator, for example, who could form the nucleus for a new and useful center of research. In other cases colleges may be able to strengthen their research programs materially by the purchase of a few hundred dollars worth of needed equipment.

Strong emphasis on support for institutions proper began early in the 1960's. Programs for computational facilities (starting in 1956), graduate science facilities (1960), institutional grants for science (1961), university science development (1965), departmental science development (1967), and college science improvement (1967) are currently in operation. These institutional base grants make available to colleges and universities amounts in direct proportion to their total NSF project grant support during the previous year.

In 1966, the House Subcommittee on Science, Research, and Development encouraged the Foundation to continue its support of institutional grants, "to open them to more than the top colleges and universities in the country, and to seek out . . . smaller institutions whose own energy and initiative indicate that with encouragement and support they can become genuine centers of excellence in research and science education."

The institutional base grant program had been useful, the subcommittee report indicated, but did not seem to have significantly narrowed the gap between the have and the have-not institutions. It said:

> The science development program has been critized as slow in getting started. While Congress showed an initial reluctance to accept this program, it now appears solidly behind it. Now the question seems to be whether the Foundation's initiative is adequate to meet national needs for institutional development. . . . Is the program limited to boosting leading institutions of the minor educational leagues into the big league of first-rate centers of excellence, or is it also intended to plant and upgrade research centers on a geographical basis so that each state, or region, has a minimum academic capability for research and science education? If the latter objective is the goal, should not it be openly identified as such?

Subcommittee members agreed that the Foundation's funding of institutional grants was insufficient. During hearings, the director of the Foundation called their attention to the problems that project grants do not help or do, in fact, intensify, and advocated expanded institutional grants as the remedy. The problems he identified included: (1) the lack of flexibility at the department level within the university; (2) the difficulties of supporting general, or centralized services (such as computers and libraries); (3) the difficulty of supporting interdisciplinary units or programs; (4) the emphasis on quality which often causes younger, unknown investigators from smaller colleges to have trouble obtaining support; and (5) the danger of subtle distortion of science through the tailoring of requests to areas where support is likely.

The National Science Foundation is not, of course, the only federal agency furnishing institutional support to the universities and colleges. The National Institutes of Health, the Department of Defense, the Office of Education, and the National Aeronautics and Space Administration have similar programs. The Office of Education, unlike the other agencies, is starting at the bottom with what one writer calls the "real academic Appalachia," and providing help to several hundred small colleges. NSF and NASA both are particularly concerned with grants in pursuit of excellence. At present, however, all five agencies are assisting institutions from the very lowest level of competence to those already so close to excellence that they can achieve first rank with relatively little aid.

LEGAL AUTHORITY

Section 1862 of the National Science Foundation Act of 1950 indicated that the initiation and support of basic scientific research and the strengthening of basic research and education in the sciences were to be the principal duties of the Foundation. The act contains no specific authorization for institutional support programs, but Congress, by appropriating funds for them, has confirmed their legality.

Bills to establish programs of institutional support were proposed in the second session of the Eighty-ninth Congress (1966) and in the Ninetieth Congress (1967–68). No formal action was taken on them. One bill, introduced in both Congresses by Representative George P. Miller of California, chairman of the House Committee on Science and Astronautics, was entitled the National Institutional Grants Program Act. In the declaration of purposes, it was stated that the mission-oriented project grant and support system had been inadequate as the sole means for federal support of research in the universities, and that stable, long-range funding must be provided as a supplement. The bill contained authorization of

$150 million for each of the first five fiscal years. The formula for distribution of funds was rather complicated, but its theory was simply to provide a broad base for grants, taking into account undergraduates, graduate students, and volume of research. The program would be administered by the National Science Foundation with a National Institutional Sciences Council as an advisory agency. In an article in *Science,* May 20, 1966, John Walsh discussed the bill at some length. Even though prospects for its immediate enactment were poor, he considered that it was significant as the most concrete expression to date of the growing demand for a major modification of the existing system of institutional support. In his opinion, the major movers in the campaign for more clearly defined institutional support had been the university administrators—he mentioned particularly the National Association of State Universities and Land Grant Colleges. Scientists in general appeared to be satisfied with the existing system, presumably fearing that the proposed new program of institutional grants would divert funds from the familiar well-established project grants system.

FINANCES

The rapid increase in programs of institutional support is shown in the Foundation's obligations for 1963–66:

1963	$44,329,386
1964	50,014,316
1965	60,236,979
1966	78,376,104

Estimates for 1967 and 1968 were in excess of $111 million.

Actual obligations of the Foundation for the fiscal year 1966 are presented in Table 11.

The Foundation's recognition of the need to strengthen institutional capabilities is clear; its rapidly expanding budget for programs for institutional support demonstrates this. The remainder of this chapter contains brief descriptions of the existing programs and their rapid growth in the 1960's.

TABLE 11
Institutional Support for Science

Program	Amount
Institutional science improvement	
Institutional science development	
University science development	$36,375,000
Department science development	2,367,429
College science improvement	0
Subtotal	38,742,429
Academic computational facilities	988,800
Total	39,731,229
Maintaining institutional strength in science	
Institutional grants for science	14,517,899
Graduate science facilities	16,216,676
Academic computational facilities and operations	7,910,300
Subtotal	38,644,875
Total	78,376,104
Less 2d stage grants for graduate laboratories to	
be obligated in fiscal year 1968	0
TOTAL	$78,376,104

UNIVERSITY COMPUTING FACILITIES

The Foundation's grants for computer facilities, which totaled less than $3 million in 1962, had increased to nearly $9 million in 1966—a measure of the importance the Foundation and the universities attach to this type of assistance to research. In 1966, thirty grants were made. Smaller educational institutions do not need, nor can they afford, complete individual computing facilities. The Foundation has helped to meet their needs by providing a single, large, central facility to be used by a group of neighboring institutions. A recent grant of $1.5 million was made in support of the Triangle Universities Computation Center (TUCC), chartered by North Carolina, North Carolina State University, and Duke University. A large central computer is linked with smaller computers located on each of the three campuses. Additionally, all North Carolina institutions of higher learning, through the use of local operating stations connected to the TUCC facility by telephone lines, will be able to explore the uses of the digital computer in the educational process. Many educators now feel that every college student should have some contact with a computer as a part of his general education. A very large-scale educational computer network was being planned in 1967. The principal sponsor, Interuniversity Communications Council, requested a $100,000 grant from the Foundation to construct and put into operation a modest pilot-scale "Edunet," based on a compact among twenty universities under which each would undertake to permit the others to use its own computer as well as its codes. While this mini-Edunet was being used as a preliminary to the original, larger Edunet concept, the council would continue its efforts to try to find funds for it. Such support could come from member universities, foundations, or the federal government. The problem is one of coordinating a number of federal agencies that might provide partial support. Without congressional action, no single agency with the possible exception of NSF or the Office of Education, would have sufficient funds to finance the large Edunet.

GRADUATE SCIENCE FACILITIES PROGRAM

This program furnishes special assistance in improving and enlarging scientific laboratories. Forty-seven institutions received grants totaling approximately $25 million in fiscal year 1966. Some of these grants were for very large projects, some for rather small ones. For example, the California Institute of Technology received $635,550 for construction of a physics research laboratory, and $64,500 to renovate facilities in research laboratories for study of the molecular basis of the control of genetic activity. By way of contrast, the University of Minnesota received $9,350 to renovate the laboratory facilities for the graduate program in chemistry at the Duluth campus.

INSTITUTIONAL GRANTS FOR SCIENCE

These grants provide institutions participating in the Foundation's research-oriented programs with funds awarded on a formula basis for general support of their scientific programs rather than for specific projects approved by the Foundation. The formula, using total research grants as a base, is tapered to favor the less well-supported institutions. In fiscal year 1966, grants were awarded to 401 colleges and universities in a total amount of $14.5 million. Using a single state as an example, in Maryland the following grants were made:

Goucher College	$23,525
Johns Hopkins University	123,347
Mount St. Agnes College	4,200
University of Maryland	115,935

SCIENCE DEVELOPMENT PROGRAM

This program, often referred to as the "centers of excellence" program, has as its purpose the upgrading of the quality of a limited number of institutions, which have demonstrated their potential for advancement. Twenty or more American universities are presently judged to be of the highest quality in science, and the Foundation's program is designed to raise other universities into this top category. In fiscal year 1966, ten universities were added to the list of institutions receiving this type of grant—the University of Arizona, University of Southern California, University of Florida, Purdue University, Louisiana State University, Tulane University, Rutgers (the state University of New Jersey), Polytechnic Institute of Brooklyn, University of Rochester, and North Carolina State University at Raleigh. Total grants of almost $64 million were made to seventeen institutions in 1965 and 1966.

Recently, the Foundation made a grant to Brooklyn Institute of Technology for a laser development program to be operated by six basic-research scientists who had left industry because they felt that their company was becoming less interested in fundamental research.

DEPARTMENTAL SCIENCE DEVELOPMENT PROGRAM

There are many colleges and universities that do not have the general strength to be developed into "centers of excellence" under the Science Development Program but do have science departments with the potential of high quality. It is anticipated that successes in the departmental science development program will stimulate broader development of the universities in which these superior departments are located. In 1966, the program was planned to operate through grants for a three-year period and for a maximum of $600,000 each. Estimated costs for fiscal year 1967 were $15 million.

The College Science Improvement Program

The upgrading of programs of science instruction in predominantly undergraduate institutions was the purpose of a new program, funded at $10 million in 1967. The first grants, as reported in *Science* (June 23, 1967), totaled nearly $2 million and went to the following: Clark University, geography, $563,740; Drexel Institute of Technology, materials engineering, $527,700; University of New Mexico, mathematics, $550,000; Tennessee Technological University, mechanical engineering, $300,000.

New Proposals

Philip Handler (chairman of the biochemistry department of Duke University, chairman of the National Science Board, and member of the President's Science Advisory Council) included an important discussion of institutional development and funding patterns in a 1967 *Science* article. The five-point funding program he proposed was based on the general principle that we should preserve the merits of the project grant system while developing mechanism for the transfer of funds to the universities in larger amounts than are customary today. He wrote:

1. Unusually large facilities which serve the national scientific community, whether radio telescopes, accelerators, or sociological data banks, and so on, are most appropriately managed by consortia of universities, in-house federal laboratories, or single universities serving as federal agents.

2. Grants for general university subvention, blocks of faculty

salaries, construction, libraries, large computer centers, institutional science development, shops, animal or other large special facilities should be conveyed to the university president or the appropriate dean.

3. Block grants to provide, *inter alia,* stipends for graduate students, general research services and the research expenses of junior members of the faculty should be made available to department chairmen or their equivalent. Instead of the widespread practice of supporting graduate research assistants with stipends derived from research grants made to their mentors or expanding current federal competitive fellowship programs by more than an order of magnitude, graduate students should be supported almost entirely from such departmental grants, an extension of the concept established in the present insufficiently funded training grants of NIH and NSF.

4. Funds appropriate to the unique requirements of the individual investigator should be awarded in his name, after assessment by the now traditional peer-judgment system. Most of the other grant mechanisms should rest on assessment of the collective ability of the applicant group in question (a department, school, or university).

5. Although some postdoctoral fellows might continue to derive their stipends from research grants, funding through the departmental grants or through an enlarged national fellowship program is much to be desired. In any case, there should be explicit recognition of the fact that it is in the career interest of young investigators, at this stage, to engage in a significant amount of formal teaching.

VIII

Science Information Activities

A frequently quoted section taken from the Foundation's first report (1950–51) sums up the purposes of its science information activities in words that adequately describe not only the early intentions of the Foundation but also the activities conducted to date:

In a sense, scientific information is both the beginning and the end product of research. . . .

Scientific progress is cumulative. One individual builds on the findings of other individuals or groups; his work in turn becomes modified or augmented by still others. The faster and more freely information passes from scientist to scientist, the faster science progresses. When this intellectual exchange is hampered, science as a whole declines. Ready exchange of information, then, can be called the circulatory system of a healthy and vigorous scientific body.

Serious problems exist in the dissemination of scientific information both internally in the United States and in obtaining for American scientists the benefit of scientific information developed in foreign countries. Publication of research papers in the learned journals is now subject to delays up to several years. Technical difficulties in abstracting published articles and in distributing abstracts among scientists further delay the proper correlation or research activities throughout the world.

Efficient dissemination of scientific information guarantees against wasted effort. No scientist will knowingly undertake study already adequately covered. His professional standing depends upon his capacity for sound and original work, and he risks that standing by duplicating the work of others. A free flow of information among working scientists provides the best insurance against duplication and overlap in research.

The activities of the Foundation in carrying out this early statement of its purposes are currently described under four headings—(1) systems development and improvement; (2) science information research and studies; (3) support of publication and services; and (4) the Foundation's publication of the results of its own research and various reports on its programs, as well as its conduct of conferences, symposia, and advanced science seminars. These activities are described in this chapter, which also deals with the Foundation's legal authority for such matters, the financing of them, and their relationship to over-all federal information activities.

LEGAL AUTHORITY

The basic act of 1950 establishing the National Science Foundation contained two provisions defining its authority to engage in information activities:

1862 (a) (5) to foster the interchange of scientific information among scientists in the United States and foreign countries.

1870 (g) to publish or arrange for the publication of scientific and technical information so as to further the full dissemination of information of scientific value consistent with the national interest.

The Foundation carried out its activities under these provisions until 1958. In that year, the National Defense Education Act (Public Law 85–864) was enacted, containing provision for a National Science Service in the National Science Foundation. Through the new service, the Foundation is required to "(1) provide, or arrange for the provision of, indexing, abstracting, translating, and other services leading to a more effective dissemination of scientific information, and (2) undertake programs to develop new or improved methods, including mechanized systems, for making scientific information available."

This law established a Science Information Council consisting of four ex-officio members (the Librarian of Congress, the director of the National Library of Medicine, the director of the Department of Agriculture Library, and the head of the Science Information Service) with fifteen members appointed by the director of the National Science Foundation—six in the fields of fundamental science, six in the fields of librarianship and scientific documentation, and three "outstanding representatives of the lay public who have demonstrated interest in the problems of communication." It also provided for terms of office, compensation and allowance for expenses, and meetings. The duties of the council were defined—to advise, to consult with, and to make recommendations to, the head of the Science Information Service.

Since 1958, each President of the United States has acted to improve the coordination of scientific information services in the federal government. Under the title "Improving the Availability of Scientific and Technical Information in the United States," the President's Science Advisory Committee in 1958 issued a report emphasizing the need for a united, efficient, and comprehensive scientific information service but concluding that a new agency would not have to be created for this purpose. The report recommended the establishment of the Science Information Service within the Foundation as an extension of its existing programs, to aid and co-ordinate existing government and private efforts. In January, 1959, the President in a letter to the Foundation asked it to implement this plan. A few weeks later, Executive Order No. 10807 (which also established the Federal Council for Science and Technology) clarified the Foundation's leadership role, providing that the Foundation should exert leadership in the coordination of the scientific information activities of the federal government, and providing that the federal agencies should cooperate with and assist the Foundation in the performance of this function.

Reorganization Plan No. 2 of 1962 considerably changed the Foundation's authority by transferring from it to the newly established Office of Science and Technology (OST) those functions relating to coordination of federal policies for promotion of basic research and education in the sciences, and those relating to evaluation of the scientific research programs of the federal agencies. Coordination of information activities was not specifically mentioned, but this activity was an integral part of the broad area of coordination of federal scientific activity for which the OST assumed responsibility.*

FINANCES

The early reports of the Foundation indicate the small size of its information activities by the amount of expenditures— $69,700 for "dissemination of scientific information" in fiscal year 1952. By 1957, the amount had increased to $994,736; in 1962, it was $7,531,171; in 1966, it was $11,620,086. The details of the 1966 expenditures, as reported in the form used by the House Committee on Appropriations in its hearings on appropriations for 1968 are shown in Table 12.

In the hearings on the NSF budget for 1968, there was discussion of requests for additional funds for systems development and improvement, for the support of publications and services, and for translation of scientific information in foreign languages.

FEDERAL INFORMATION ACTIVITIES

Today, the science information activities of the National Science Foundation constitute only one part—and not a major one—of the extensive information services offered by the various federal departments and agencies. This fact makes it difficult to consider the Foundation's activities as a separate subject, because there is so much collaboration and coordination

---

* Mention should be made here of the Foundation's limited authority to classify materials, as defined in Chapter 15, National Security, of Title 50 of the U.S. Code; Executive Order No. 10501, Safeguarding Official Information (November, 1953); and several later amendments to the order. Three groups of executive departments and agencies are given the power to classify defense information or material. The first group has primary responsibility for matters pertaining to national defense, and their officials or delegated representatives are authorized to classify information as provided in the law. The second group, having partial but not primary responsibility for matters pertaining to national defense, includes the National Science Foundation, and only the heads of agencies—not their delegates—may classify information. Those in the third group have no authority to classify unless it has been specifically granted.

TABLE 12
Expenditures for Science Information Activities, 1966–68
(in Millions of Dollars)

Category of Support	Fiscal Year		
	1966	1967*	1968*
Discipline-based information systems			
Support of publications and services	$3.3	$4.0	$3.2
Systems development and improvement	1.9	2.9	5.8
Science information research and studies	0.9	0.6	0.6
Subtotal	6.1	7.5	9.6
Federal science information activities			
Support of publications and services	1.8	1.0	2.1
Science information research and studies	0.2	0.5	1.0
Subtotal	2.0	1.5	3.1
General science information activities			
Support of publications and services	0.2	0.1	0.2
Systems development and improvement	0.6	0.5	0.5
Science information research and studies	2.7	1.2	1.2
Subtotal	3.5	1.8	1.9
TOTAL	$11.6	$10.8	$14.6

* Estimated.

that the part carried out by any one agency is usually not clearly defined. Table 13, which presents a percentage distribution of (estimated) federal financial obligations for scientific and technical information by agency and activity for fiscal year 1966, gives an idea of the complexity of this subject.

It will be noted that five agencies (the departments of Defense, Commerce, HEW, and Interior, and NASA) accounted for about 90 per cent of activities in publication and distribution and that in the other categories the great majority of expenditures was made by a few departments and agencies, with the Department of Defense usually the major contributor. The National Science Foundation expended only 6 per cent of the total expenditures for 1966.*

* Expenditures in each of the four categories mentioned in Table 13 were as follows: publication and distribution, $75 million; documentation, reference, and information services, $126 million; symposia and audio-visual media, $35 million; research and development in information sciences, documentation, and information systems, $24 million. Total expenditure for all four categories was $261 million.

TABLE 13
Percentage Distribution of Federal Financial Obligations for
Scientific and Technical Information, 1966

Agency	Publication and Distribution	Documentation, Reference, and Information Services	Symposia and Audiovisual Media	Research and Development in Information Sciences Documentation, and Information Systems	Total*
Defense	28	40	50	53	39
Commerce	33	11	2	4	16
HEW	6	13	23	14	13
NASA	13	8	12	2	10
NSF	2	6	4	18	6
Agriculture	3	7	4	1	5
Library of Congress	—	10	†	2	5
Interior	9	2	2	3	4
AEC	3	1	1	3	2
Other	2	1	3	1	1

* Total is not 100 per cent because of rounding.
† Less than 0.5 per cent.

In describing the organization of the federal government's information systems, the position of the Committee on Scientific and Technical Information (COSATI) must be particularly emphasized. It is a permanent working group within the Federal Council for Science and Technology composed of senior federal department or agency officials responsible for operation of scientific and technical information systems. It is a mechanism to insure interagency program coordination and development of government-wide standards and compatability among information systems. COSATI's objective is to develop an articulated but decentralized federal system designed to provide an important tool for improving research and development both in and out of the government.

The Foundation participates in the Federal Council itself and in COSATI as "one among equals" and has no special functions or powers. In retrospect, it is not hard to understand why the Foundation was unable to coordinate and evaluate the science information activities of all the federal departments and agencies. Their activities were closely related to their major functions and in many cases were far more extensive than those of the Foundation—a new and small agency. Coordination, if it was to be effective, had to be established in a location superior to *all* the departments and agencies, and this was accomplished by the provisions of Reorganization Plan No. 2 of 1962, establishing the OST, the Federal Council, and COSATI.

SYSTEMS DEVELOPMENT AND IMPROVEMENT

Currently, the term "explosion" is being used to refer to any situation growing at such a rapid rate that it either is—or will become—a threat to the public. We have the well-publicized "population explosion" and, in the present connection, there is much discussion of an "information explosion." Whether "explosion" is too strong a term can be questioned, but there is no doubt that the accelerated rate of publication of scientific information is increasing already existing difficulties in collecting, storing, retrieving, and disseminating this information, and that steps must be taken to develop and improve the systems in order that scientists may be able to use the results of research.

An editorial in *Science,* October 7, 1966, described the divergent opinions concerning the seriousness of the information explosion. Many researchers find that most of their needs for information are met by scanning the relatively few journals in which material of interest to them is usually published. But there are those who believe that we are failing to utilize much of the vast information available in the 50,000 scientific journals published regularly in the world. Some politicians, the editorial stated, have "an almost pathological fear that research may be unwittingly duplicated" and are willing to support all kinds of attempts to make information more readily available, thus leading the federal government to devote $250 million annually to such efforts—a sum that "substantially exceeds the funds allocated for all research project grants supported by the National Science Foundation."

The National Science Foundation has, during its entire history, considered development and improvement of systems for handling scientific information one of its important functions. Its first annual report said:

The Foundation will also sponsor research to develop new techniques for the quick and economical dissemination of scientific information. This research will be designed to improve existing methods of abstracting information, to study the use of mechanical and electronic means for compiling bibliographies and other reference materials, to encourage more rapid ways of preparing and processing reports and other units of scientific literature, and to design better methods for making these units of scientific literature available to scientists.

Its sixteenth annual report stated:

The Foundation's science information activities are directed toward making the results of research readily available to this country's scientists and engineers. To reach this goal, the Foundation is concentrating its efforts on developing effective and comprehensive information systems serving the scientific disciplines, and establishing workable relationships between the information systems of the professional community and those largely mission-oriented systems maintained by federal agencies. . . .

Many scientific organizations and commercial firms operate information systems that serve relatively homogeneous populations of users. Many federal agencies (e.g., HEW, NASA, AEC, Department of Agriculture) operate mission-oriented information systems. That much duplication of input and output effort occurs among Federal and non-Federal systems is accepted as a fact, and there is an urgent need to enlarge, modernize, and coordinate them.

It is clear that the role most appropriate for the Foundation is the strengthening of discipline-oriented systems, and enabling those responsible for them to establish interconnections among and between them and the Federally operated systems. More than $6 million (52 %) of the available fiscal year 1966 funds were expended in discipline-oriented activities.

A section of the 1966 report commented on the progress of national information systems, largely resulting from the Foundation's support, and included a brief account of NSF's collaboration with COSATI and with the Committee on Scientific and Technical Communication, established by the National Academy of Sciences and the National Academy of Engineering.

The director of the Foundation explained in some detail the plans in support of systems improvement that the Foundation wished to carry out in fiscal year 1968 with the increased appropriation for that purpose requested in its 1968 budget. Quoting from the hearings before the subcommittee of the House Committee on Appropriations, the director said:

> The fortunate thing is that the advent of the electronic computer makes it possible to think of much more systematic and effective ways of doing this. This whole problem has been studied very carefully within the executive branch and by some committees of Congress and as a result there has emerged a plan that goes something like this:
>
> There will be a movement toward computerized systems in each of the various branches of science. They will be of two kinds. It is just a little bit like library cataloging, if you will. It is much more complicated but it is that type of thing. There will be systems which will relate to a given scientific discipline such as mathematics or physics or chemistry, and so on. Then there will be other systems that will relate to the uses of information, such as medicine, which cuts across these others.

The director's statement continued with description of the different information systems that are the responsibility of the Foundation itself and of the Public Health Service, the Department of Agriculture, and the Atomic Energy Commission, as examples. Central monitoring of the different programs is the function of the Foundation. The other part of its role is the development of individual systems in the basic sciences, and the director described progress in development of such a system for chemistry, with beginnings in systems for physics and engineering. The Foundation finances most of this work, which is largely carried out by professional societies. The different agencies within the executive branch, working closely with the Office of Science and Technology, cooperate with the Foundation in monitoring such programs to assure that there is compatibility between them. Although this problem was difficult, its solution, in the director's opinion, was long overdue.

SCIENCE INFORMATION RESEARCH AND STUDIES

The activities of the Foundation that are included in this classification accounted for $2.2 million in 1967, and the Foundation asked for about a half-million-dollar increase for fiscal year 1968. The program encourages and supports studies of communication patterns and the use of information among scientists and engineers; it seeks to improve information retrieval; it evaluates information systems and their components; and it establishes and supports science information centers in universities.

Some examples will illustrate the kinds of projects included in the program. The University of Chicago Library received a grant of $118,000 to assist in developing a computerized bibliographical data system. This furnished partial support for the first year of the projected three-year plan. The proposed system, it was hoped, would be operational by the time the University's new library building—containing research libraries in the social sciences and the humanities and the Graduate Library School—was completed. The final system would make it possible for a reader, by means of a typewriter keyboard or similar device connected directly to a computer, to ask this basic computer store for the titles and locations of relevant books and other data and information.

A grant of $66,225 to the Center for Research Libraries was to be used to investigate the costs and service characteristics of alternative methods of making scientific literature available to scientists. The users of research libraries will be delighted to know that the principal factor to be studied was the time which elapses between the scientist's request for an item and its delivery. Two centers, one at the University of California (Los Angeles) and one at Ohio State University, had been established as science information research centers. Each year the Foundation reports the grants and awards it has made, and those that are clearly for research in information science are fairly easy to identify. A few examples are cited from the listing for 1966:

U.S. Department of Commerce–National Bureau of Standards
Research and development in the chemical information program: 12 months, $110,000.

American Geological Institute
Establishment of a cooperative, computer-based information service in the solid earth sciences: 21 months, $748,000.

Herner and Company
Contract for a survey and study of nonconventional technical information systems: 8 months, $4,353.

Syracuse University
User study of translated Soviet scientific journals: 4 months, $2,940.

Social Science Research Council
Preparation and publication of "Bibliography on Modern Chinese Society": 22 months, $77,200.

These examples illustrate the wide range of support ($2,940 to $748,000) and the variety of institutions and subjects included in the grant program for science information service.

Support of Publication and Services

The Foundation provides assistance to scientific societies, universities, and other nonprofit organizations for the purpose of increasing the availability of scientific literature to American scientists and engineers. The principal activities supported by this program include: (1) publication of existing journals, monographs, and volumes of conference proceedings; (2) occasionally, establishment of new scientific journals in research fields not adequately covered by existing journals; (3) publication of abstracting and indexing volumes, including specialized ones in areas not adequately supplied; (4) support provided to the major U.S. scientific societies for translation, publication, and distribution of significant foreign literature; (5) coordination and administration, on behalf of eleven federal agencies, of the Special Foreign Currency Science Information Program, which is financed under Public Law 480 with excess foreign currencies that have accrued to the credit of the U.S. government from sales of surplus agricultural products in Poland, Yugoslavia, and Israel; (6) preparation and dissemination of guides and directories; (7) operation of science information centers; and (8) compilation, publication, and distribution of the Foundation's publications, "Current Research and Development in Scientific Documentation," "Non-conventional Scientific and Technical Information Systems in Current Use," and "Scientific Information Notes."

In 1967, the Foundation was allowed over $5 million for these activities, and it requested a more-than-$300,000 increase for fiscal 1968. In addition to the amount appropriated to itself, the Foundation expends considerable amounts transferred from other federal agencies—for example, for administration of Public Law 480 activities.

A sampling of Foundation-supported projects in 1966 illustrates the preceding summary statement of its activities:

Yale University
Publication of Peabody Museum of Natural History *Bulletin:* 36 months, $77,200.

Wayne State University
Comprehensive electronic data processing of two Russian lexicons: 12 months, $116,500.

Library of Congress
National Referral Center for Science and Technology: 12 months, $7,913.

Smithsonian Institution
Contract for operation of the Science Information Exchange: 12 months, $1,902,356.

Nolit Publishing House, Yugoslavia
Contract for translating and printing in the English language scientific and technical journals, series, books, monographs, and such other materials as are mutually agreed upon: no time specified, $290,000 (a Public Law 480 project).

Engineers Joint Council
Improvement and extension of source-indexing practices of selected engineering journals: 12 months, $35,725.

PUBLICATIONS OF THE FOUNDATION

The National Science Foundation has its own series of publications, many of which have been used in the preparation of this book. There would be little use to include a complete list at this point, because so many of the publications are no longer available, and, in all probability, collections in libraries are incomplete. The Foundation publishes a list of its currently available publications, including the prices of those that must be purchased from the superintendent of documents at the Government Printing Office. The list can be obtained from the publications section of the Foundation. The May, 1967, list of available publications was arranged under several headings:

Annual Reports
Including grants and awards and the annual weather modification report.

Descriptive Brochures
Eleven were listed, mostly small pamphlets describing science education programs.

Science Education Announcements
Periodically, announcements of programs are issued: schedule of NSF programs for education in the sciences, graduate education in science, fellowships, graduate

traineeships, undergraduate education in science, college teacher programs, undergraduate research participation, instructional scientific equipment, and precollege education in science.

Science Resource Studies

Ten bulletins called "Reviews of Data on Science Resources" were listed, nine "Manpower and Education Studies," seven "Research and Development Economic Studies," three "Foreign Science Resource Studies," and nine "Special Studies."

Science Information Notes

A bimonthly periodical reporting national and international developments in scientific and technical information dissemination.

Science Information Activities of Federal Agencies

A series of pamphlets describing the policies and practices of federal agencies relative to their scientific and technical information activities.

Documentation Research

Periodic reports on current research and development in scientific documentation.

Information Systems

Occasional reports on nonconventional scientific and technical information systems in current use.

CONFERENCES, SYMPOSIA, AND ADVANCED SCIENCE SEMINARS

The National Science Foundation does not have specific legal authorization for initiating or supporting or conducting scientific meetings; there is no single identifiable appropriation for them; and in the organization of the Foundation there is no one division or section administering them. The conferences, symposia, and seminars are means by which the Foundation carries into operation its delegated functions. Consequently, their financing and administration are parts of many different operations.

The first institutes sponsored by the Foundation, in 1953,

were summer conferences or institutes for college teachers of science. A year later, similar institutes for high school teachers were held. In 1956–57, academic-year institutes were inaugurated. These educational institutes have been so successful that their number has increased rapidly.

In 1953, the Foundation sponsored eight research conferences. In 1966, the number was eighty-one, in the following general fields and with the following numbers of conferences and symposia:

Biological and medical sciences	31
Engineering sciences	14
Environmental sciences	9
Mathematical and physical sciences	22
Social sciences	5
Total	81
Advanced science seminars	31
Total	112

Many different subjects were dealt with in the conferences, symposia, and seminars. By way of illustration, the following list includes the first meeting listed in each of the categories:

Biological and Medical Sciences
Environmental Influences on Reproduction Processes; Michigan State University, East Lansing, Michigan, July 30–31, 1965; Chairman: William Hansel, Cornell University; Sponsor: American Society of Animal Science.

Engineering Sciences
Conference on the Application of Engineering Problems to Appalachia; Morgantown, West Virginia, August 2–5, 1965; Chairman: Chester A. Arents, West Virginia University; Sponsors: Engineering Foundation and West Virginia University.

Environmental Sciences
Weather Modification Section of the Fifth Berkeley Symposium on Mathematical Statistics and Probability;

Berkeley, California, June 21–July 18, 1965, and December 27–28, 1965; Chairmen: Lucien M. LeCam and Jerzy Neyman, University of California, Berkeley; Sponsor: University of California, Berkeley.

Mathematical and Physical Sciences

Fifth Berkeley Symposium on Mathematical Statistics; Berkeley, California, June 21–July 18, 1965; Chairmen: Lucien LeCam and Jerzy Neyman, University of California, Berkeley; Sponsors: Office of Naval Research, Air Force Office of Scientific Research, and University of California, Berkeley.

Social Sciences

Research Conference on Political Data; Ann Arbor, Michigan, July 26–August 13, 1965; Chairman: Warren E. Miller, University of Michigan; Sponsor: Interuniversity Consortium for Political Research.

Advanced Science Seminars

International Field Institute; Brazil, June 18–August 1, 1966; Director: J. Van N. Dorr II, U.S. Geological Survey, Washington, D.C.; Grantee: American Geological Institute.

IX

International Science Activities

The axiom that "science knows no frontiers" is, like many axioms, more an expression of principle than of fact. Particularly during periods of war (hot or cold), there are, in fact, many frontiers binding scientists rigidly. During World War II, German scientists and American scientists were closely contained within their respective geographical boundaries and were not free to communicate with fellow scientists outside. Today, Chinese scientists are as closely restricted.

Nevertheless, over a long period of time and taken on the whole, the axiom is true. This is the case for a variety of reasons. In the first place, no scientist of any nation can prevent a scientist of another nation from making the same discovery of scientific fact he has made. Such duplicating has, in fact, often occurred. Furthermore, continued scientific research is based on accumulated prior research, and shutting up portions of it within national frontiers prevents incorporation of those portions in the general body of scientific fact available to all scientists for use in their studies. Finally, many scientists believe that international scientific cooperation is one way to increase all types of cooperation and thus prevent war.

This situation raises some nice questions that have been and are much discussed concerning the values of international scientific cooperation. In general, if we consider the United States' present participation in all sorts of international scientific programs, examine our past history, listen to statements of public officials and private citizens—including scientists, particularly—in short, if we take a good look at the evidence, the conclusion must be that we have been and are consistently trying to remove the frontiers that might bind science and that we believe this to be in the best interest of science itself and, more practically, in our best interest as a nation.

A group of scientists from the United States, Soviet Union, France, Belgium, Italy, and Wales who had helped to organize the International Geophysical Year and the Years of the Quiet Sun, in a statement to *The New York Times* (July 27, 1966), the *Times* of London, and other newspapers two years ago, urged that such cooperation be made permanent. They said, in part:

> These worldwide cooperative scientific projects have shown conclusively that however many and serious are the political problems that trouble the human race, it is possible for all the nations of the world to work closely together in great enterprises for the common good.
>
>   . . . we feel that not only will the rapid advance of geophysical science be maintained, but, more importantly, it is certain that this continued close cooperation between men of science from all parts of the world will make a significant contribution to the wider field of human understanding and goodwill.

There is, undoubtedly, much agreement with this statement, and there is also disagreement. The British scientific journal *Nature* (in many ways like the American *Science*) published a brief article in its issue of June 4, 1966, entitled "Is Science Really International?" which offered a very different opinion:

> Received doctrine holds that science is in some sense supranational. Ever since Davy and Farady went jaunting in Europe at the height of the Napoleonic Wars, it has been permissible to pad out public speeches with declarations that "science knows no frontiers" or that "the laws of physics are the same the whole world over." As a result, the idealism of young people has been harnessed to the view that science is potentially a substitute for diplomacy. Teach enough people enough physics, and international tensions will melt away in a flood of reason. That is how

the theory goes. It is a puzzle to know how it can be so widely held when there is so much evidence to contradict it.

. . .

Science may be the same everywhere, but the institutions of science are not organized for a common attack on the common problems. On the contrary, international rivalry, even chauvinism, is rife. Nobel prizes, like Olympic gold medals, are regarded as feathers in national caps. For various reasons, not all of them pleasant, international collaboration as it exists is much less real, and much less effective, than it could be.

The remainder of the article dealt with several ways in which Western Europe could quickly multiply the benefits of present collaboration and in conclusion expressed hope that certain efforts of the British Council on Scientific Policy might induce European colleagues "to put stuffing into the old and most empty boast that science is already international."

Another opinion on international science activities was expressed by a subcommittee of the Committee on Science and Astronautics of the House of Representatives in House Report 1236 (1966), which recognized that national foreign policy included scientific activities as an important element in foreign relations. The role of the National Science Foundation in this regard was yet to be crystalized, the report said, but from the director's standpoint there were four areas that were or could be the basis for NSF programs: (1) international cooperative research programs, such as the International Geophysical Year, the Antarctic research program, or the international Indian Ocean expedition; (2) purchase from abroad of research services unavailable here, or that can be done better there; (3) support of science and science education in developing countries; and (4) support of science activities abroad to promote American foreign policy objectives.

The director of the Foundation posed this question: "Should we, other things being equal, support some science in some place where our foreign policy objectives would be helped, even though we could get it done just as well at home?" He went on to say: "I think this is a question that would be fruitful for Congress to think about—how the objectives of science and the objectives of foreign policy can be combined effectively and appropriately."

The development of the international science activities of the Foundation from 1950 to the present would in itself be a major study, too long to be undertaken in the present instance. Current activities are numerous; their number and size are increasing; the prevailing opinion is that further increase will occur and should be supported. The Foundation's international science activities are of two types: those funded by the NSF, which have the basic intent of strengthening American science; and those funded by the Agency for International Development, which are directed toward assisting certain foreign countries to develop their scientific resources.

In 1966, the Foundation summarized the two types of activities undertaken as means of strengthening American science:

Research-Related Support

The regular support programs for the Foundation may provide funds for research conducted abroad or in collaboration with foreign scientists, for attendance at international scientific meetings, for international exchange of scientific information, and for participation in education and training programs. Few NSF grants are made to foreign institutions and only when exceptional conditions justify U.S. support to the foreign recipient. . . .

Although NSF awards are rarely made to international scientific organizations, U.S. organizations (principally the National Academy of Sciences) are provided support to maintain adequate representation of U.S. scientific interests in the deliberations and programs of private international scientific organizations, such as the International Council of Scientific Unions, the International Federation for Documentation, and the Pacific Science Association.

Education-Related Support

Contacts between individual American and foreign scientists are encouraged and supported through fellowship and exchange programs. Of the 4,336 fellowships awarded in fiscal year 1966 to U.S. citizens, 256 provided for tenure at a foreign institution; 66 U.S. citizens received NSF-administered North Atlantic Treaty Organization Fellowships for study in institutions of other NATO member countries. Under the NSF Senior Foreign Scientist Fellowship Program, provision was made for 51 American institutions to be visited by that number of eminent foreign scholars. Under the NSF-supported program for exchange of scientists between the National Academy of Sciences, U.S.A., and the Academy of Sciences, U.S.S.R., there was participation by 18 American and 23 Soviet scientists. Travel grants were provided to 67 young American scientists for attendance at 41 Advanced Study Institutes sponsored by NATO.

Other travel grants enabled approximately 646 American scientists to visit locations abroad, principally for the purpose of attending international scientific meetings. A total of 121 foreign educators were placed in NSF-sponsored teaching institutes held at various U.S. colleges and universities. In addition, a number of these institutes were served by visiting foreign lecturers.

The Foundation continues to act as a catalyst in developing more significant involvement of American agencies in international organizations with broad scientific missions, such as UNESCO and OECD, and it coordinates the various science interests of the American agencies in the international organizations.

The Office of International Science Activities was established in 1961. Today, it has five subdivisions responsible for International Science Development, International Organizations Staff, Program Analysis Staff, the U.S.–Japan Cooperative Science Program, and the Science Liaison Staff (in New Delhi, San Jose, and Tokyo).

This chapter treats the NSF's different international activities, the legal authority and financing of them, and problems resulting from these activities.

LEGAL AUTHORITY

The National Science Foundation is given the authority, in general terms, to support basic scientific research through contracts, grants, loans, and other forms of assistance. Possibly this provision alone would have been sufficient to authorize the different international activities of the Foundation, but the law contains several other specific grants of authority. Certain sections of the National Science Foundation Act of 1950, as amended, other statutes, executive orders of the President, directives of the Federal Council for Science and Technology and the Bureau of the Budget, and internal directives from the Foundation define the Foundation's authority.

One section of the basic law, entitled "International Cooperation and Coordination with Foreign Policy" (section 1872), contains the principal provisions relating to that function. The Foundation is authorized to cooperate with international scientific activities consistent with its purposes as set forth in the basic law. With the approval of the Board, the director may pay the expenses of American representatives to accredited international scientific meetings. With the approval of the Secretary of State, the Foundation may grant fellowships to foreign nationals for scientific study or work in the United States. The authority to enter into arrangements with foreign organizations or individuals, and to cooperate in international scientific activities is exercised only with the approval of the Secretary of State "to the end that such authority shall be exercised in such manner as is consistent with the foreign policy objectives of the United States." Negotiations with foreign countries or agencies in carrying out such activities shall be carried out by the Secretary of State in consultation with the director.

Other provisions of the basic law contain specific references to international aspects of various activities: (1) interchange of scientific information among scientists in the United States and foreign countries (1862(5)), (2) award of scholarships and graduate fellowships (1869), (3) contractual powers of the Foundation (1870(c)), and (4) contractual powers of the Foundation (1873(g)).

The Bureau of the Budget has established procedures for control of federal expenditures abroad, has limited the Foundation's expenditures for project grants in certain countries, and has stressed the need to limit fellowships to U.S. citizens deciding to study abroad. The Federal Council outlined procedures for support by federal agencies of research in foreign institutions. Executive orders have assigned to the Foundation responsibility for administering foreign scientific translation programs for several federal agencies.

Changes in the basic law relating to international activities were contained in Public Law 90-407, enacted in 1968. The new provisions, broadening the Foundation's authority, are discussed in the concluding pages of this chapter.

FINANCES

Because almost every activity of the Foundation has at least a few international aspects, it is difficult to determine exactly how much of its funds are expended in this area. In 1967, the House Committee on Science and Astronautics published a report entitled "The Participation of Federal Agencies in International Scientific Programs." The portions relating to the Foundation form the basis for much of the information in this chapter.

The first major international program in which the Foundation participated was the International Geophysical Year (IGY), 1957–58. The Foundation obligated over $43 million, in addition to the $100 million provided by other federal agencies, for the entire program.

In fiscal year 1966 the Foundation, in programs that it funds directly—the so-called mission-related programs—obligated $20,687,999; in programs administered by the NSF but funded from other sources the total was $1,569,570; the grand total was $22,257,269. Table 14 shows the actual expenditures.

NATIONAL RESEARCH PROGRAMS
INVOLVING OTHER NATIONS

The national research programs have been described in some detail in Chapter V, but several of their activities involv-

TABLE 14
NSF Expenditures for International Science Activities, 1966

Activity	Amount
Mission-related (NSF-funded) programs	
International science education	
Foreign educators	$854,386
U.S. organizations and personnel	
overseas	2,618,455
Subtotal	3,472,841
Research abroad	
Foreign institutions	534,650
U.S. organizations overseas	1,528,840
Subtotal	2,063,490
International science information	
Translations	1,735,476
Foreign science information	248,399
Travel and exchanges	763,763
Studies of foreign science and	
technical resources	158,048
Subtotal	2,905,686
International research programs	
U.S.–Antarctic research program	8,362,896
International Year of the Quiet Sun	1,617,283
U.S.–Japan cooperative science	
program	708,846
International Indian Ocean	
expedition	1,067,707
Subtotal	11,756,732
International science liaison	
National Academy of Science	565,600
Other	13,450
Subtotal	579,050
Less amount included in international	
research programs	− 89,800
Subtotal	489,250
Total	20,687,999
NSF-administered programs	
funded from other sources	
NATO and OECD fellowships	483,670
Science information translations	647,800
NSF-AID science education assistance	437,800
Total	1,569,270
TOTAL	$22,257,629

ing the participation of other nations deserve additional attention.

The International Geophysical Year is probably the best known and most successful of the international research programs. Under it, for the third time in a century, scientists of many countries joined to conduct a worldwide study of the planet Earth. The first Polar Year (1882–83) and the second Polar Year (1932–33), as their names indicate, were studies of the regions of the North Pole. In 1950, plans were initiated for a comprehensive international research effort to be held in 1957–58, because maximum solar disturbances were predicted in that period. The American participants were organized in the U.S. National Committee for the Geophysical Year, established by the National Academy of Sciences, to represent the United States in the International Council of Scientific Unions and to coordinate the American effort. The National Academy of Sciences–National Research Council formally requested the National Science Board of the National Science Foundation to obtain and administer the federal funds necessary to carry out the American efforts. Scientific planning and coordination were furnished by a special committee of the National Academy.

The financing of this project illustrates the complexities involved when many government departments and agencies and private institutions cooperate. About one-third of the total cost was specifically appropriated by Congress for the IGY, to furnish special stations and facilities. This amount was $43.5 million for the 1955–58 period. Existing programs in public and private laboratories contributed another third, and the remaining third was furnished by private institutions, particularly the universities. Technical and logistics support was furnished by the Department of Defense—for example, $34.2 million was appropriated for the U.S. scientific satellite in appropriations for the Department of Defense for 1958. The difficulty in estimating the total costs to the United States also is found in estimating the total costs for all the nations participating in the project. These estimates range from $750 million to $1.5 billion, including logistics support.

As for the project itself, sixty-six nations participated in it and from 20,000 to 30,000 scientists and technicians were estimated to have made observations at more than 4,000 stations. Many fields of the earth sciences were included—astrogeophysical measurements, meteorology, oceanography, glaciology, ionospheric physics, aurora and airglow, geomagnetism, cosmic rays, and rocket exploration of the upper atmosphere.

Three world data centers were established to acquire complete sets of all IGY data—one in the United States, one in the Soviet Union, and one operated by Western European and Pacific nations. A particularly interesting American contribution to the program was the design and launching of the first successful U.S. earth satellite on January 31, 1958. The Soviet Union had surprised both scientists and laymen by orbiting a much larger satellite in the preceding October. The repercussions of these two achievements are still felt today, and there is no doubt that they furnished the strongest impetus to the movement for increased support for aid to basic research and for development of scientific manpower, evidenced in the increase in growth of the Foundation in the following years.

The dramatic success of the IGY resulted in enthusiasm both among scientists and the general public, and the pattern of international cooperation in a scientific program was established. Special international committees were created after 1958 to continue collaboration in oceanic research, atmospheric research, and space research.

At the close of the International Geophysical Year, almost all the participating nations conducting research in Antarctica during the IGY continued their Antarctic programs, and on December 1, 1959, twelve of these nations signed the Antarctic Treaty guaranteeing free access to the entire continent and providing for unlimited inspection of all installations. (Incidentally, this treaty contained the only nuclear test ban in existence at that time.) The National Science Foundation was assigned responsibility for planning, coordinating, managing, and funding American programs in Antarctic research; the Department of Defense budgets for them and provides logistic support (chiefly through the Navy), and the Department of State is responsible for effecting over-all coordination. The Committee on Polar Research of the National Academy of Sciences makes broad recommendations and indicates possible new areas of research. The actual work on the various programs is done by scientists from universities, government laboratories, and other research centers. The Foundation has a 266-foot research vessel *Eltanin* as a floating mobile research station. There are four mainland stations—McMurdo, Pole, Byrd, and Palmer—and a number of inland stations.

Funds for the program in recent years have ranged from $6 million or $7 million to $64 million in 1966. During fiscal year 1966, a total of 135 grants and contracts was awarded at a cost of $8.4 million, and it was reported that twenty-eight American scientific parties had been in the field during the season. Americans served with parties from Argentina, Australia, Chile, Japan, South Africa, and the Soviet Union.

The international Indian Ocean expedition was another continuation of the international cooperative research programs that began with the IGY. Responsibility for coordinating the federal effort and for funding the programs was assigned to the NSF by President Eisenhower in June, 1960, and President Kennedy endorsed it in his message to Congress in March, 1961.

The Indian Ocean covers 14 per cent of the earth's surface, thus making a large research effort necessary. The thirteen participating nations expected to realize both scientific and long-range economic benefits, and their contributions during the five-year period made possible extensive research into topography and circulation of the ocean and the distribution of plant and animal life in it. Forty-one ships of cooperating nations, manned by scientists from twenty-eight countries, took part.

The United States carried out its part of the program through the Department of the Navy, the Coast and Geodetic

Survey, the Bureau of Commercial Fisheries, and the National Science Foundation. Special committees of UNESCO supplied international planning; the National Academy of Sciences was the communications medium with one UNESCO committee; the State Department had policy functions in relation to UNESCO, which it delegated to an international panel of the Federal Council's Interagency Committee on Oceanography.

The U.S. contribution of funds amounted to about one-third of the total during the 1962–65 period, and its contribution for the entire period (1961–66) was more than $20 million. There were fourteen American ships and five aircraft in operation, and the United States made fourteen cruises to the area. Field operations were concluded in 1966, but the processing of the immense amount of data is requiring continued NSF grants or contracts with other federal agencies. Two volumes of collected reprints of individual articles were published in 1966, but this represents only a small portion of the expected scientific results.

Some of the outstanding projects were the discovery of the East Indian Ocean ridge; studies of ocean currents, countercurrents, upswellings, and monsoons; and the establishment of the Indian National Institute of Oceanography, for which scientists from the United States made major contributions in assisting India.

In 1961, President Kennedy and Premier Hayato Ikeda, in recognition of the importance of broadening educational, cultural, and scientific cooperation between the United States and Japan, agreed to form two joint committees, one of which was to seek ways to strengthen scientific cooperation. Upon their recommendation, there was established in 1963 the United States–Japan Committee on Scientific Cooperation. Because this committee is not an administrative body, the Secretary of State requested the NSF to coordinate the research interests of the United States.

The Foundation evaluates and verifies the desirability and practicability of participation in proposed projects, provides funds for support of projects under its jurisdiction, and provides funds to support projects of other Federal agencies until they can pay for them under their own budgets. The program is cooperative both scientifically and financially, with each country supporting its own citizens. There have been three types of projects—cooperative research projects, visits by scientists of one country to the other to conduct research or to lecture, and scientific seminars, conferences, and planning meetings.

Since the beginning of the program, more than fifty projects have been started, nineteen of them in 1966. Annual U.S. costs have approximated $700,000 since 1963, and many scientists from the two countries have exchanged visits. In 1966 alone, thirty new cooperative research projects were initiated, and twenty-eight meetings were sponsored, mostly in Japan.

Naturally, the research programs have included many co-operative studies in the Pacific area, as, for example, research in earthquakes, hurricanes, and typhoons; clouds and rainfall mechanisms; origins of volcanoes and hot springs; effects of ocean ice on weather; oceanographic studies; and relation-ships between fauna and flora of the two countries. The medi-cal sciences and education in the sciences have also been the subjects of cooperative projects.

In 1962, President Kennedy authorized U.S. participation in a program with the exotic title of International Years of the Quiet Sun (IQSY), and he designated the Foundation as the agency to finance and coordinate it. The IGY program had collected information during a period of maximum sunspot activity, and the IQSY was timed for a period of solar repose from January, 1964, to December, 1965, which was later ex-tended to 1967. The first full year of the program was com-pleted during 1965 but observations were extended beyond that date, and additional time was needed to assemble the results and, during 1966 and 1967, to analyze them. Publica-tion of consolidated scientific results were to appear in 1968 and 1969.

Like the IGY, the IQSY is an international cooperative

effort in which scientists from more than sixty nations are studying global geophysical phenomena. Over-all coordination has been carried out by the IQSY Committee of the International Council of Scientific Unions, and in the United States by the U.S. Committee for IQSY of the Geophysics Board of the National Academy of Sciences. The key point is that the observations must be based on simultaneous observations of related phenomena all over the globe, and this is accomplished through international agreements to make the observations in coordination, and to forward them to world data centers established for this purpose, in order that they may be available to scientists.

The American program has included observations in the fields of meteorology, geomagnetism, aurora, airglow, ionospheric physics, solar physics, cosmic rays, and aeronomy. Many different agencies have conducted the observations—stations of the Weather Bureau, the Central Radio Propagation Laboratory, the U.S. Coast and Geodetic Survey, the National Aeronautics and Space Administration, and the research laboratories of the Department of Defense.

Scientific Research in its issue of June, 1967, reported that, as the IQSY was approaching a close, the groundwork was being laid for building a completely new scientific subdiscipline—solar-terrestrial physics—on an international scale. This would include studies of the interaction between the earth's atmosphere and the sun. A new permanent organization was emerging as a full-fledged member of the International Council of Scientific Unions, and the National Academy of Sciences had set up a new committee for the new subdiscipline. The new NAS committee will advise the National Science Foundation and other federal agencies. Most of the research funds will come from the NSF.

The United States and thirty-two other countries are cooperating in another venture called the International Upper Mantle Project. The National Academy of Sciences—National Research Council prepared the over-all plans for U.S. participation and then asked the Foundation to obtain endorsement, which came from the Special Assistant to the President for Science and Technology, in April, 1962. The Geological Survey, the Coast and Geodetic Survey, the Advanced Research Projects Agency of the Department of Defense, and the National Science Foundation are primarily responsible.

In January, 1963, the cost of the three-year program was estimated at approximately $31 million, for which the Foundation's support was derived from its funds for basic research. (In the case of the other programs described in this section, the funds expended were expressly approved by the President and Congress.)

The purpose of this program is to determine the composition, structure, and dynamics of the crust and the upper portions of the mantle of the earth, through a concerted worldwide field and laboratory attack on the largely unsolved problems in the earth sciences. Practically, the program provides for cost-sharing in the conduct of investigations outside the United States. Its results will be related to those obtained from domestic projects, such as the Ocean Sediment Coring Program which is solely supported by the United States.

The U.S. Upper Mantle Committee, which was formed by the National Academy in 1962, published its second progress report in November, 1967. The report, presented at the XIV General Assembly of the International Union of Geodesy and Geophysics in Switzerland, summarized some 315 projects included as part of the U.S. program and presented a review of findings in its first three years of operation. Proposals for the 1966–70 phase of the U.S. program include studies of the continental margins and island arcs of the world rift system, extension of the U.S. Transcontinental Geophysical Survey into the Atlantic Ocean, and drilling in water and on land for scientific purposes.

The four national research centers supported by the National Science Foundation are U.S. government-owned installations, each managed by an independent nonprofit corporation composed of associations of universities. Three of them are used almost entirely for domestic research, although some foreign scientists and students visit them, use their facilities, and attend seminars. The fourth center, the Cerro Tololo Inter-American Observatory in Chile, meets the needs of astronomers in both North and South America, providing for investigation of phenomena visible only in the Southern Hemisphere, and for correlation with observations made at the observatories in the Northern Hemisphere. A small permanent staff operates the observatory. Most of the observing time is available to astronomers from North and South America.

In 1967, President Johnson of the United States and President Eduardo Frei of Chile jointly announced that a new telescope was to be built at the Observatory. The 150-inch reflecting telescope—the largest in the Southern Hemisphere—will be similar to the 150-inch telescope at Kitt Peak Observatory near Tucson, Arizona. The National Science Foundation and the Ford Foundation are financing the construction at Cerro Tololo. Kitt Peak and Cerro Tololo both are operated by the Association of Universities for Research in Astronomy, a consortium of nine U.S. universities working under contract with the Foundation.

The newest of the Foundation's national research centers is the one for atmospheric research in Colorado, established in 1960. It is operated, under contract with the National Science Foundation, by the nonprofit University Corporation for Atmospheric Research, representing twenty-three universities with graduate programs in this field. A large proportion of its work is domestic, but one project, involving several large-scale meteorological experiments is expected to culminate in a global atmospheric research project by about 1972. This will be an international undertaking comparable to the International Geophysical Year, with other countries, Federal agencies, and universities cooperating in large-scale meteorological projects on an international scale.

INTERNATIONAL SCIENCE EDUCATION PROGRAMS

In 1959, the Foundation began to develop international science education programs under three general groupings—

curricula development programs, teacher training programs, and science student programs. Limited support was given to several special pilot programs, which might lead to permanent operational programs. Also in 1959, Congress passed Public Law 86-232, containing an amendment broadening the Foundation's powers to participate in international scientific activities. Previously, these activities were characterized by a one-way flow, but the new authority permitted the Foundation to start some cooperative programs in which a two-way flow led to exchanges benefiting both American and foreign science educators. (One early example was the inclusion of more than seventy teachers from abroad in the 1960 NSF summer institutes.) The three types of programs initiated in 1959 were continued in 1960, and a fourth, the international cooperative program, was added. The story in the following years is an account of increased support and of additional programs.

The budget for NSF's international science education programs, financed by its own funds and those transferred from other agencies, is shown in Table 15.

Reporting on its own program for 1966 in international science education activities, the NSF listed projects at Stanford University, the University of Colorado, the Pan-American Union, the American Chemical Society, the American Express Company, Educational Services, Inc., Oklahoma State University, University of Texas, University of São Paulo, Sociedad Chilena de Química, and Instituto Para la Promoción de la Enseñanza de las Matemáticas in Peru. It also listed all fellowship and traineeship awards offered, by program and field, in 1966. This included fifty-one senior foreign scientists—ten in engineering, three in mathematical science, eighteen in physical sciences, fifteen in life and medical sciences, and five in social sciences and psychology. The senior foreign scientists were from many countries—one each for Brazil, Canada, Costa Rica, Egypt, India, Ireland, Israel, Italy, the Netherlands, Poland, Switzerland, and Yugoslavia; two each for Belgium, Czechoslovakia, France, and Scotland; three for

TABLE 15
NSF International Science Education Budget

Activity	1965	1966	1967*
Mission-related			
International science education†			
Foreign educators			
Senior foreign scientist fellowships	$660,583	$672,550	$649,400
Visiting lecturers, institutes	79,670	60,650	59,600
Foreign participants, institutes	146,854	121,186	121,000
Subtotal	887,107	854,386	830,000
U.S. organizations and personnel overseas			
Organization for tropical studies	50,490	416,750	0
U.S. fellows overseas	2,191,518	2,201,705	1,900,000
Subtotal	2,242,008	2,618,455	1,900,000
Total	3,129,115	3,472,841	2,730,000
NSF-administered‡			
NATO and OECD fellowships	425,775	483,670	328,000
NSF-AID science education assistance	658,958	437,800	320,000
Total	1,084,733	921,470	648,000

* Estimated.
† NSF funded.
‡ Funded from sources other than NSF.

Australia and Sweden; five for West Germany; seven for Japan; and thirteen for the United Kingdom.

EXCHANGE OF PERSONS

The Foundation's activities in the international and foreign fields include exchange of persons and exchange of information. It is impossible to determine exactly the numbers of Americans going abroad or the numbers of foreigners coming here under financing from the Foundation, because these movements occur as parts of almost all of its programs. But, as an example, expenditures for senior foreign scientists' fellowships, and the visiting lecturers and participants in institutes were $854,386 in 1966. In the same year, $2,618,455 was spent for American organizations and personnel overseas, in science activities, and travel and exchanges under the international science information programs totaled $763,763. Also in 1966, the Foundation supported a large number of scientific conferences, symposia, and advanced science seminars—so many, in fact, that merely listing them in the Foundation's annual report required nearly ten pages. Undoubtedly, foreign lecturers and participants attended a large number of these meetings, many of which are identifiable as being international. Several of them were held abroad.

The Foundation grants funds for travel to individual scientists and to scientific organizations, particularly for attendance at foreign and international meetings. Since most individuals cannot afford the heavy expenses of foreign travel, and few universities have adequate funds for such use by their faculties, this service of the Foundation is particularly valuable to university faculty members. A few examples from 1966 will illustrate the types of grants: a grant of $780 to the University of Arizona for travel by a member of the faculty to the Second International Conference on Palynology in the Netherlands; $35,000 to the American Psychological Association for attendance of its members at the Eighteenth International Congress of Psychology in Moscow; several grants for attendance at the International Symposium on Volcanology in New Zealand, including three for members of university faculties, four for members of the U.S. Geological Survey, and one for a representative of the Carnegie Institution; and grants to sixty-seven young American scientists for attendance at forty-one advanced study institutes sponsored by NATO.

Unfortunately, some characteristics of international meetings indicate that the Foundation should use a degree of caution in making it possible for Americans to attend them. Of course, the first criterion is the public good to be gained by sending the particular applicant for a travel grant to the meeting which he proposes to attend. The Foundation is spending the public's money and it must take into consideration more than the possible value to the individual scientist. As for the meetings themselves, it is quite clear that, just because they furnish international contacts, there is no certainty that their conduct will result in valuable scientific interchange. An editorial in *Science* (October 10, 1966) discussed this problem:

> When conducted under optimum conditions, international scientific meetings provide a splendid setting for constructive interchange. As important as formal sessions is discussion in small groups and person-to-person. Such contact permits mutual quick evaluation of quality of mind and character. Judgments can lead to long-lasting confidence. In a world ceaselessly troubled by tensions and antagonisms, international friendships should be fostered.
>
> But most international meetings are not conducted under optimum circumstances. Indeed, Americans who complain about their own national meetings find that, by comparison, the large international gatherings held abroad are often a shambles. The complaints are many. Under unfavorable circumstances the visiting scientist is harassed almost endlessly. There are problems about visas and travel. Housing reservations are not honored, and the visitor is consigned to a third-class hotel far from the meeting. Advance programs are not available, and no one seems to know where and when sessions will be held. When a schedule is available, it is not honored. No central directory of participants is maintained, and personal interchange is difficult.
>
> To the long list of annoyances a new one has been added, which could destroy the possibility of holding truly international meetings. The new factor is the injection of cold-war politics. This year five major international meetings were held in Russia. Four were marred by controversial political activity.

However, the editorial mentioned grounds for hope that excessive cold-war activity can be arrested, through the influence of the National Academy of Sciences and the International Council of Scientific Unions and concluded: "The total direct and indirect costs of international congresses amount to tens of millions of dollars a year. The congresses are too costly and too potentially valuable to be allowed to be marred by mediocre arrangements or cold-war political activity."

The scientific exchange visits between the United States and the Soviet Union, which are financed by the Foundation, are

administered in the United States by the National Academy of
Scientists and by the Academy of Sciences in the Soviet Union. The two academies first signed an agreement in July,
1959, covering a two-year period and providing for exchange
visitors from each side who would lecture, observe research,
and attend scientific meetings. The program began on a rather
small scale in 1960 and has been continued. In 1966, the
Foundation furnished $272,375 for American participation.
In 1966, the Foundation also furnished funds ($75,000) for
similar exchange programs with Poland, Yugoslavia, Ru-
mania, Hungary, and Czechoslovakia.

In order to prevent excessive gold flow from the United
States, these exchange programs are financed in a special way.
Thus, if an American goes to Russia, the United States pays
his round-trip travel expenses, and the Russians pay his expenses while he is there. If a Russian comes here, the reverse
is true.

INTERNATIONAL INFORMATION SERVICE

Acting under its authorizations "to foster the interchange
of scientific information among scientists in the United States
and foreign countries" and to publish or arrange for the publication of scientific and technical information, the Foundation in its earliest years began to establish a foreign science
information program. The amounts of money available were
small. In fact, in 1952 a total of only $69,700 was obligated
for *all* scientific information. Ten years later, some $9 million
was expended, including more than $700,000 for interna-
tional scientific information exchange. Title IX of the National Defense Education Act of 1958 included provision for
strengthening the information functions of the Foundation. In
the years immediately following the passage of this act, expenditures for all the different forms of information services
increased rapidly, to over $5 million in 1960.

Illustrative financial data for 1965–67 (estimated) are presented in Table 16, taken from a report of the House Committee on Science and Astronautics that dealt with the participa-

TABLE 16
NSF Expenditures for International Science
Information Programs, 1965–67

	1965	1966	1967*
Translations			
Domestic	$751,995	$770,476	$1,000,000
Public Law 480	1,000,000	965,000	1,000,000
Subtotal	1,751,995	1,735,476	2,000,000
Foreign science information	464,885	248,399	160,000
Travel and exchanges	683,815	763,763	800,000
Studies of foreign science and technical resources	122,000	158,048	125,000
TOTAL	3,022,695	2,905,686	3,085,000

* Estimated.

tion of federal agencies in international scientific programs (1967). Travel and exchanges, in Table 16, includes activities that could be classified just as appropriately under other major headings—for example, "education"—because the funds used for travel and exchange of scientists largely benefit the universities and their faculties.

The activities included in the Public Law 480 projects are those financed under the authority of the Agricultural Trade Development and Assistance Act of 1954, as amended, under which the President is authorized to:

. . . use or enter into agreements with friendly nations or organizations of nations to use the foreign currencies, including principal and interest from loan repayments, which accrue under this subchapter for one or more of the following purposes:

. . .

k. To collect, collate, translate, abstract, and disseminate scientific and technological information and to conduct research and support scientific activities overseas including programs and projects of scientific cooperation between the United States and other countries such as coordinated research against diseases common to all of mankind or unique to individual regions of the globe, and to promote and support programs of medical and scientific research, cultural and educational development, health, nutrition, and sanitation: Provided, That foreign currencies shall be available for the purposes of this subsection (in addition to funds otherwise made available for such purposes) only in such amounts as may be specified from time to time in appropriation acts.

The appropriation acts for fiscal years 1961 through 1967 included provisions for such appropriations—$1.6 million in 1961, $1.8 million in 1962, and $1 million in all later years —for the uses defined in section (k).

The Foundation's program activities under the Public Law 480 projects were defined in its 1962 annual report:

1. To promote effective acquisition of foreign scientific publications through purchase and by exchange between U.S. and foreign organizations.

2. To provide data to the U.S. scientific community on sources and availability of foreign scientific information, which includes support for scientific and technical reference aids.

3. To increase the scope and quantity of translations of the most important foreign scientific publications.

4. To stimulate cooperation with international organizations in support of projects which will add to the U.S. store of information and materially improve scientific communication on an international scale.

One of the principal problems in making foreign scientific materials available to American scientists is the matter of language, because relatively few of them can use materials written in any language except English. In 1966, a total of $1,735,476 was spent in support of domestic translation projects ($770,476) and Public Law 480 projects ($965,000). The domestic projects included translations of the entire contents of many periodicals and selective translation of separate articles; support of the abstracting, indexing, and bibliographic services of several American scientific societies; and preparation of directories of foreign scientists and bibliographies of special subjects. The Public Law 480 projects consisted of a translation program utilizing excess foreign currencies owned by the United States (the so-called counterpart funds), which can be expended only in the country of origin.

The funds were divided among projects in Israel, Yugoslavia, and Poland for translation of materials, mainly in the Russian and East European languages.

The NSF is the coordinating and administering agency for the scientific translation requirements of the major executive departments and agencies, under the authority of two executive orders, and translation and other information services are based chiefly on Russian, East European, Chinese, and Japanese publications, which constitute about one-third of all scientific literature. All translation services of the Foundation are carried out in close cooperation with American scientific societies.

Grants are given to the science information programs of international nongovernment organizations, such as the International Federation for Documentation and the Abstracting Board of the International Council of Scientific Unions, and the Foundation works with such international governmental organizations as the Organization for Economic Cooperation and Development, and with the different executive agencies in their participation in international scientific and technical information services.

In 1966, grants were made to the Canadian Mathematical Congress, the International Council of Scientific Unions, the International Association for Plant Toxonomy, the Central Institute for Scientific, Technical, and Economic Information (Warsaw), the Nolit Publishing House (Belgrade), the Indian National Scientific Documentation Center (New Delhi), the Israel Program for Scientific Translations (Jerusalem), and the Japan Documentation Society (Tokyo). Many grants were also made to American universities, executive agencies, professional societies, and research management companies for projects related to foreign information services.

ASSISTANCE TO FOREIGN INSTITUTIONS

Basic research in foreign institutions is supported under some circumstances, but only if it is directly related to the promotion of science in the United States, and if it meets the strict conditions laid down by the Foundation. In 1966, there were twenty-eight awards to foreign institutions, totaling $684,000. The Foundation has established definite criteria for awarding such grants. The proposed support must be in consonance with the prevailing research policies and practices of the particular foreign country; the project must be directly pertinent to the Foundation's responsibility for supporting science in the United States; the project must be one which can be carried out more effectively by a foreign institution than by an institution in the United States; the possibility that the foreign country might support the project must have been explored and found inadequate; the investigator must be of outstanding competence for performance of the research; unique facilities or geographic location must be essential contributing factors to accomplishment of the work; and the institution to be supported must offer significant training to American scientists.

Participation in the Work of
International Agencies

The Foundation's association with different international agencies in their scientific programs frequently takes the form of assisting American participation by selecting our representatives, briefing them, and furnishing documents for use in meetings. NSF grants are rarely made directly to international organizations. Usually American organizations (frequently the National Academy of Sciences) maintain adequate representation of our scientific interests in the work of such private international organizations as the Organization for Economic Cooperation and Development (OECD), the Organization of American States (OAS), the United Nations Economic, Scientific and Cultural Organization (UNESCO), the International Council of Scientific Unions (ICSU), the North Atlantic Treaty Organization (NATO), and the International Federation for Documentation. In general, the NSF coordinates the various interests of the American agencies in such international science activities, and the Department of State is responsible for diplomatic activities.

Working with the Department of State, the Foundation has assisted the OECD by helping with American activities in the Organization. It cooperates with UNESCO in connection with science teaching and information, and with NATO in its advanced training program.

When, on October 2, 1964, President Johnson issued a proclamation stating that the United States would participate in the International Cooperation Year 1965 (an event established by the United Nations to publicize the immense amount of cooperation in all fields taking place among nations, as well as to develop new programs), thirty-one committees were established by the U.S. government to work on various aspects of this project. Two of the committees—Science and Technology, and Manpower—were chaired by NSF personnel, and staff members were members of several other committees. A White House Conference on the International Cooperation Year, 1965, considered the committee findings.

So many federal departments and agencies carry on research activities abroad that it is not easy to discover the extent to which they cooperate with the Foundation in them all. The State, Defense, Agriculture, and Health, Education, and Welfare departments in particular offer many instances. Probably the Foundation's relationships with the Department of State and with the Office of Science and Technology in the Office of the President are the most significant.

The Department of State must take into account scientific developments in connection with its primary responsibility for formulating and carrying out foreign policy, and it is also responsible for American participation in international organizations. The United States is a member of some sixty-five of these, and probably at least half of them have scientific activities. The Department of State has a chief science advisory post—that of director of international scientific and international affairs—and the Foundation has an Office of International Science Activities. The cooperation between these two is continual and important but of a nature not publicly disclosed.

The Foundation has an agreement with the Agency for International Development (AID) to assist in the advancement of science education in the developing areas of the world. With funding from AID, the Foundation has administered such programs in India and in several Latin American countries. These programs are coordinated with related programs of the Ford Foundation and those of several international organizations.

The influence of the U.S. Congress on the Foundation's international activities is exercised in the same ways that it is on all other matters relating to the Foundation (see Chapter XII), but occasionally there is, in addition, congressional interest in an international subject affecting the Foundation directly or indirectly. A few examples may be cited. In recent years, these have included enactment of the International Education Act of 1966, consideration of legislation to control the "brain drain," and recommendations by a committee of the House of Representatives concerning the "dollar drain" and its effect on our balance-of-payments deficit. Congressional concern with these three subjects indicated that although Congress continued to favor international education programs (approval that by implication covers science programs) members had begun to realize that some new types of controls would have to be devised to counter unexpected and undesirable byproducts.

SOME SPECIAL PROBLEMS

The problems arising from the international exchange of personnel, including of course scientists, are common to many agencies of the government and nonprofit organizations that support exchange programs. These problems are not well defined as yet, since they were not foreseen and have become apparent only fairly recently. The most conspicuous is the brain drain—a phenomenon produced by young people who go to an advanced country to be educated under special programs, with the expectation that they will return to their homes and there make available their new skills but who choose instead to remain in the land of their education because of better opportunities for personal advancement. A second result is the dollar drain, which results from U.S. assistance to persons, either Americans or foreign citizens, who receive research grants in American money, including provision for conducting research (and thus expending the money) outside the United States.

In each case, a benefit to an individual carries with it a result that may not be in the general interest. If we are trying to aid an underdeveloped country through provision of educational training in American institutions for some of its citizens, we do not achieve our purpose if those persons stay in this country after the training is concluded. If grants of American dollars for research to be expended abroad have an adverse effect on our balance-of-trade, that fact cannot be overlooked solely because the projects are worthwhile from the researchers' standpoints and from the standpoint of the advancement of knowledge.

A very careful balancing of advantages and disadvantages in various international research and education programs is necessary, and safeguards must be established to insure that the intended results are, in fact, obtained and undesirable side-effects controlled.

There is a general belief that the main responsibility for keeping highly skilled people from emigrating and for insuring that those who study abroad do return rests with the countries of origin. The United States can, of course, exert influence on foreign students largely through private individuals, as their teachers, to return home, by emphasizing their patriotic duty or by refusing to offer them permanent employment. The United States can also help countries of origin to provide better opportunities for the use of the persons whom they have permitted to study abroad, as a means of encouraging their return. Perhaps the concern over the undesirable effects of the situation condemned by being dubbed a brain drain may have concealed the good effects. By no means would it be desirable —even if it were practically possible—to stop the migration of scholars and students. In *Science* (November 25, 1966), Dael Wolfle discussed various means for reducing the flow of talent from the poorer to the wealthier countries:

> We should not, however, try to stop migration. Scholars have always been a migratory lot—to Alexandria, Rome, Baghdad, Paris, and other centers, and now to western Europe and North America—and no one can contend that the world would now be better off if the migrants had been forced to stay at home. Reduction of migration must not stop the free movement of scholars, artists, artisans, and other venturesome souls within or across national boundaries.

However, Wolfle noted that Great Britain was studying her loss of medical talent, the Pan American Health Organization has studied migration of professionals from Latin America, the Council on International and Cultural Affairs of the U.S. government had held a conference on the migration of talent and skills, and Title III of the International Education Act of 1966 required a study of migration from the developing countries to the United States. Several other studies have been published or are in preparation. The Inter-Agency Council on International Education and Cultural Affairs, after a two-year study, published its report in April, 1967. *The New York Times* had a series of five reports by Bernard D. Nossiter in its issues for February 12–16, 1967. In 1967, the National Science Foundation published a report entitled "Scientists and Engineers from Abroad, 1962–1964," the fourth publication in which the Foundation has presented periodic reviews of the subject.

The dollar drain, or balance-of-payments deficit, has lasted for some years and has not responded markedly to efforts to reduce it. In February, 1965, President Johnson launched a new drive, and after that time he repeatedly urged and ordered federal departments and agencies to limit overseas expenditures, whether large or small, to urgent and nonpostponable projects. It is still alleged that there is sufficient drain from American science activities abroad to warrant taking action.

The Research and Technical Programs Subcommittee of the House Committee on Government Operations published a report on "plugging the dollar drain" in April, 1966. They questioned the continued dollar financing of foreign research abroad, of American scientists training outside the United States, and of overseas science offices, which together resulted in an annual drain of about $35 million. The report described projects that the subcommittee considered to be nonurgent but which were still being financed under the headings of foreign research projects, science training abroad, and overseas offices. The National Science Foundation supports all three types of projects.

The subcommittee concluded then that controls on foreign research (criteria governing approval of projects and ceilings on expenditures) were "loose and haphazard" and that American initiatives to expand research abroad without a dollar drain were insufficient. The report said that far greater efforts could be made to increase research support by the OECD countries, both in the developed and in the poorer countries. It also expressed the belief that support by other countries of research or of scientists visiting in the United States had not been adequately sought and that in countries where the United States owned excess local currencies (then over $1.5 billion) the American agencies sponsoring research abroad had not taken full advantage of these holdings.

During 1967, and particularly in 1968, Congress was increasingly concerned about reduction in the national budget and about improvement in the balance of payments. Inevitably, appropriations for science activities, including those of an international or foreign nature, were affected. Up-to-date figures on the National Science Foundation's foreign expenditures are unavailable or incomplete, but it can be stated that its support of projects for scientific research and study abroad has been reduced.

The problem of overseas social science research has also caused serious embarrassment to the National Science Foundation and others. The Foundation, which furnished funds for overseas research in increasing amounts each year, has had much the same kind of difficulty in connection with projects of this kind that the Department of Defense, the Department of State, the Central Intelligence Agency, and AID encounter with social science research projects to be carried out abroad by American researchers. Despite several recent unhappy examples, there is general agreement that such projects are a necessary and desirable means of accomplishing the major purposes of these agencies, but that some controls must be instituted to prevent possible hostility and suspicion resulting in undesirable effects on international relations. The National Science Foundation, of course, is not financing projects as a *means* of carrying out its functions, as are the four agencies named above. Rather, the financing of projects per se is the Foundation's function. This constitutes a rather important difference.

Particularly since 1965, debate on this subject has involved the foreign countries in which American social science research is being conducted by various federal agencies, the agencies themselves, members and committees of the Congress, individual researchers with private or government grants or contracts, and the press and various publications. Indirectly, the entire situation has affected the National Science Foundation, even though there has been only one conspicuous case in which a person with a Foundation grant aroused criticism.

In awarding a grant for research abroad on its established basis of the merits of the project and the abilities of the researcher, the Foundation must inevitably be aware of a third element—its probable impact on the nation's foreign relations. This consideration is present to a minor degree in the award of grants in all subject matter fields, but it is particularly apparent in the social sciences.

The best-known example of what can go wrong—and it is very well known, having received extensive treatment in the press and scientific professional journals—was "Project Camelot," a social science research project conducted in Chile. It did not involve the NSF. The Department of the Army sponsored this project, which was carried out under contract by a special branch of American University, and was designed to produce a better understanding of the dynamics of revolution in foreign countries, through a study of the processes of social change and the mechanisms for the established order to accommodate change in an effective manner. The Army's increasing role in military assistance and counterinsurgency offered the justification for conducting basic research in this area. Because of the difficulty caused in Chile by this project, the Army cancelled it within a short time, but Congressional investigation followed, and there was a great deal of adverse publicity. As one result, the President directed the Secretary of State to set up machinery for clearance of all federally sponsored research abroad which might affect American foreign relations.

The National Science Foundation's operations are not subject to the control of the Foreign Affairs Research Council established after Camelot, because it did not seem suitable to impose the same review and clearance on private research projects supported by the Foundation as were deemed necessary for projects funded by operating agencies for their own purposes. However, the NSF has had its bad moments. The case of Stephen Smale will not soon be forgotten.

In August, 1966, Smale, a professor on the Berkeley campus of the University of California, caused considerable concern by his activities as a participant in the International Congress of Mathematicians in Moscow. The details of Smale's background, his relationships with the Free Speech Movement and the Vietnam Day Committee at Berkeley, his difficulties with the Committee on Un-American Activities of the House of Representatives, the financing of his attendance at the Moscow Congress (this is where NSF became involved), what he actually said and did at the Congress, what the University of California and the Foundation and certain members of Congress proposed to do about it and what they finally did, and later action taken by the National Academy of Sciences and by the executive committee of the International Council of Scientific Unions show clearly what problems can arise from the simple and blameless act of giving a college professor a small travel grant to attend an international professional meeting. Although the Smale case did not attract as much public attention as Project Camelot, the scientific and academic communities were deeply interested in it, and the University of California and the National Science Foundation treated it as a serious matter because of the principles involved.

Smale held a tenured professorship in mathematics at Berkeley, where he was involved in several academic activist movements on the campus. He was judged to be a distinguished mathematician, and he planned to attend the International Congress of Mathematicians in Moscow, where he was to deliver a paper and receive an award considered to be the "Nobel prize of mathematics." During two of his months of absence from Berkeley he was to be on so-called summer salary, to be paid from an NSF grant of $91,500 that, as principal investigator, he shared with several other mathematicians. He drew $1,000, which was specifically designated in the grant to cover his travel expenses to and from Moscow. He also received for the same purpose $400 from the National Academy of Sciences–National Research Council, which administered NSF funds designated for travel to and from the Congress. His public statements from Moscow in August, condemning the American involvement in Vietnam and other activities were reported in the American press, causing alarm in Berkeley, the Foundation, the National Academy, and, inevitably, Congress. At first, Berkeley decided to withhold Smale's August paycheck, pending an accounting of his summer months. Finally, on September 30, the university officials decided that he had properly accounted for his summer's work and sent him his pay.

The Foundation, in the meantime, had to respond to attacks by members of Congress who were incensed at the expenditure of public funds by a recipient who made an attack on American foreign policy while he was abroad. Representative Durward G. Hall (Missouri) demanded that no further grants be given to individuals whose public statements and actions are clearly intended to give aid and comfort to the enemy. The director of the Foundation replied that, on the basis of its established policy, the Foundation gives no grants to Communists, officially certified subversives, or advocates of unconstitutional change of government. While this policy might, on rare occasions, permit support of the research of a person who could be considered to have acted improperly, the Foundation said:

> . . . the policy provides a sound frame of reference for the support of unclassified research by the National Science Foundation. Under this policy, the known facts regarding Professor Smale provide no basis for termination of support to the University of California with respect to next year's summer salary to Professor Smale.

In *Science* (October 21, 1966), D. S. Greenberg wrote: "NSF, which is a very small boat on the sea of national politics, has regained its composure after a touch of panic over the Smale affair, and is honorably, though quietly, standing by the principle that, by Act of Congress, it is concerned only with the professor's mathematics, not his politics."

But NSF's problems with Professor Smale were not quite ended. His two-year grant was to expire in March, 1968. His application for a renewal asked for a grant of approximately $250,000 to be spent over a two-year period, with Smale again as the principal investigator, with a staff of five senior and three junior researchers. From August 31, 1967, when the Foundation refused to grant the request as presented, because of unacceptable administrative arrangements, to November 17, 1967, when the Foundation finally did make the grant, there were many published accounts of the difficulties the two parties were encountering, and important changes were made. The final agreement was reached by providing a grant of $87,500 to Smale, and another grant of the same amount to one of his colleagues.

Changes Resulting from Public Law 90–407

In 1968, Congress enacted Public Law 90–407, amending several provisions of the original National Science Foundation Act. Originally, the Foundation had jurisdiction over "basic scientific research activities." The new law changed this wording to "scientific activities"—a broadened authority—and authorized the NSF to undertake on its own initiative, or at the request of the Secretary of State or the Secretary of Defense, the support of scientific activities relating to international cooperation. The new authority is discretionary rather than mandatory, and provides that any such activities requested by either Secretary must be financed by funds transferred by him, must be classified, and must be identified as resulting from the Secretary's request.

In the course of preliminary hearings by the House Subcommittee on Science, Research, and Development, several witnesses discussed the new section. The director of the Foundation welcomed the revision because it would broaden the Foundation's authority to participate in international scientific activities. The acting director of the Office of International Scientific and Technological Affairs of the Department of State stated, in part:

> We understand the consequence of the proposed revision . . . is to remove the ambiguity concerning the authority of the National Science Foundation to engage in international activities at the request of the Secretary of State. The Department of State believes this clarification of congressional intent is timely and desirable. The authority which this subsection will make available will make it possible to deal more decisively than heretofore with the opportunities afforded by scientific and technological developments for international cooperation and the pursuit of U.S. foreign policies.
>
> It will permit positive action in the so-called gray areas which have thus far proven difficult to come to grips with. Furthermore, it will make possible the inauguration of new bilateral and multilateral scientific relationships which could prove to be of overriding advantage to U.S. national interest, broadly conceived.

X

Science Policy Planning

Many long articles and large portions of books have been devoted to discussions of whether the United States has a science policy, what it is, whether we *should* have one, who should make it, and so on. In spite of this overabundance of discussion and attempt at definition of science policy, it is doubtful that any one formulation could be unanimously agreed upon. For working purposes, two recent attempts from authoritative sources may be cited. Both are contained in House Report 1236 (1966).

> National science policy is a constellation of interrelated policies. These policies may be grouped together under this singular term because they affect, directly or indirectly, the level, substance, and conduct of scientific activities in the United States, the opportunities for and content of education in the sciences, and the utilization and development of the Nation's resources for science. Science policies are also shaped by State and local governments and by nongovernmental institutions, enterprises, and organizations. It is appropriate, therefore, to speak of a constellation of both public and private science policies [Dr. Leland J. Haworth, director, NSF.]

That was Director Haworth's statement. Several pages later, the following appeared:

> From the standpoint of the subcommittee, science policy is taken to mean the collection of explicit and implicit policies and programs by which science is employed in the public interest to meet specific needs. Science policy embraces the allocation of funds, manpower, facilities, and organizations, and the continuing de-

velopment of our science resources. The decentralized, even fragmented character of national science policy deserves attention because it is possible that changes in constituent policies, made for special or narrow reasons, do affect the state and quality of resources for science, and thus become the concern of the National Science Foundation.

Almost every annual report of the Foundation has contained information on the function of science policy planning. In the first annual report for 1950–51 the opening paragraph was brief and to the point, and it contained a very accurate prognostication: "The development and formulation of a national science policy will take time. At the outset it must be approached with care and thoroughness."

This sort of approach, in the Foundation's judgment, required the development of a "sound foundation of fact" which was, and still is, one of the chief tasks of the Foundation. The Program Analysis Office was established with its first duty defined along three lines: studies of existing federal, university, and industrial research support; analysis of the current status of science and research by fields of science; and special studies on urgent topics.

If the National Science Foundation had been created as the exclusive agency for federal science policy—which it was not intended to be, nor has it ever been—the history of its efforts in this field would have been very different. In a short time, it was clear that there would have to be some clarification of the policy-making responsibilities of the Foundation and the other federal departments and agencies engaged in research and development. President Dwight D. Eisenhower issued Executive Order 10521 in March, 1954, for this purpose. Section 1 contained this wording: "The National Science Foundation . . . shall from time to time recommend to the President policies for the promotion and support of basic research and education in the sciences, including policies with respect to furnishing guidance to the Federal Government in the conduct and support of basic scientific research."

In general, Executive Order 10521 broadened the scope

of power of the Foundation, but, on March 13, 1959, Executive Order 10807, which also established the Federal Council for Science and Technology, considerably cut back on this power. In particular, Executive Order 10807 contained an amendment to section 1 of Executive Order 10521, above, adding the phrase "toward defining the responsibilities of the federal government" after the word "guidance."

By 1962, additional definition of the function of science policy planning was included in Reorganization Plan No. 2, which established the Office of Science and Technology (OST) as a new unit in the Executive Office of the President, and transferred certain functions of the National Science Foundation to the new Office. President Kennedy's message of March 29, 1962, transmitting Reorganization Plan No. 2 to the Congress, explained the purpose of this transfer, noting that:

> . . . the Foundation, being at the same organizational level as other agencies, cannot satisfactorily coordinate Federal science policies or evaluate programs of other agencies. Science policies, transcending agency lines, need to be coordinated and shaped at the level of the Executive Office of the President drawing upon many resources both within and outside of Government. Similarly, staff efforts at that higher level are required for the evaluation of Government programs in science and technology.

Part I of the Reorganization Plan furnished further strengthening of science organization at the Presidential level and adjustment of the Foundation's role to reflect changed conditions:

> *The Foundation will continue to originate policy proposals and recommendations concerning the support of basic research and education in the sciences, and the new Office will look to the Foundation to provide studies and information on which sound national policies in science and technology can be based.* [Emphasis added.]

In brief summary, the plan transferred from the Foundation to the Council so much of the functions of the former provided in section 1862 (a)(1) of the National Science Foundation Act as would enable the Council to advise and assist the President in achieving coordinated federal policies for the promotion of basic research and education in the sciences. It also transferred the functions of the Foundation in section 1962 (a)(6) "to evaluate scientific research programs undertaken by agencies of the federal government."

Even with this transfer of authority, it was intended that the Foundation would continue to originate policy proposals and recommendations concerning basic research and education in science, and to provide studies and information to the OST on which it could base policies.

How, in the following years, has this arrangement for science policy planning worked out? The Subcommittee on Science, Research, and Development of the House Committee on Science and Astronautics gave a great deal of attention to the question in its hearings on the status and operations of the National Science Foundation in 1964 and 1965, and it reported its conclusions in House Report 1236 (1966).

With the functions left to it after Reorganization Plan No. 2 became effective, the Foundation remained strategically placed to initiate and help to shape national science policy. The committee was aware of the definite steps that the Foundation had taken but concluded:

. . . these steps have been halting and slow, sometimes directed more toward the academic interests of the reseachers than toward the needs of national policy, and do not reflect the priority among NSF activities that is necessary.

. . . it appears that the OST was obliged to move to fill a vacuum which occurred when the Foundation was not able to fill the policy role originally intended for it by Congress. The splintering of Federal responsibility for national science policy caused in part by Reorganization Plan No. 2 has further weakened the ability of the Foundation and the National Science Board to become leaders in national science policy.

It is the view of the subcommittee that the Foundation is now well enough established and of sufficient size and importance to resume a responsibility to develop and encourage the pursuit of national policy for promotion of basic research and education in the sciences.

This role should be reasserted. It should be reasserted both to restore to the Foundation some of the functions assigned to it by the Congress, and, still more important, to give the Foundation greater responsibility for national policy concerned with resources for scientific research—whether basic or applied—in terms of the needs of industry and government as well as the academic community.

The report continued with more specific criticism of two aspects of the Foundation's science policy planning: (1) statistics for science policy and (2) manpower information. Under both headings, the recommendation was made that the Foundation strengthen and improve its conduct of these activities because of the increasing need for such information both within and outside the government.

One of the difficulties in solving the whole problem, or complex of problems, involved in science policy planning in the federal government is the lack of studies that might serve as a basis for solution. Obviously, long-range planning cannot be performed unless there are adequate studies describing present and future needs, nor can the adequacy of present programs be evaluated.

That the foregoing discussion of science policy planning may seem to be a somewhat baffling introduction to a description of the Foundation's activities included under this title, is, unfortunately, a true presentation. Even the legal authority of the National Science Foundation with respect to science policy contains neither definition of the term nor description of the subjects to be included in it. The only practical thing to do under present circumstances is to cease further consideration of the general subject and to concentrate on what the Foundation actually does today that it considers to be science policy planning.

The following sections of this chapter deal briefly with the legal authority and finances of science policy planning by the

Foundation and with its special studies of an urgent nature, scientific manpower program, and studies of public and private funding of science, of educational and research institutions, of science policies and programs, and other activities.

The reader's attention is called to chapters XI–XIV of this book dealing with relationships among the Foundation and other agencies in the executive branch, with the Congress, the universities, the nonprofit foundations, the scientific community, and international agencies. Singly and in combination, they all determine science "policy"—or perhaps it is more accurate to say science "policies."

LEGAL AUTHORITY

The statutory authority for the Foundation's functions in the field of science policy planning is contained in Section 1862 of the U.S. Code, which authorizes and directs the Foundation

1. to develop and encourage the pursuit of a national policy for the promotion of basic research and education in the sciences;

2. . . . to appraise the impact of research upon industrial development and upon the general welfare;

. . .

6. to evaluate scientific research programs undertaken by agencies of the Federal Government . . . ;

. . .

8. to maintain a register of scientific and technical personnel and in other ways provide a clearinghouse for information covering all scientific and technical personnel in the United States, including the territories and possessions.

Under Executive Order 10521 of 1952, as amended by Executive Order 10807 of 1959, as discussed already, the Foundation was directed to "recommend to the President policies for the promotion and support of basic research and education in the sciences, including policies with respect to furnishing guidance toward defining the responsibilities of the Federal

Government in the conduct and support of basic scientific research."

Sections 2–10 of the amended order provide in considerable detail for the Foundation's preparation of studies and recommendations, review of basic scientific research programs of all federal agencies, cooperation with these agencies, and for the Foundation's "leadership in the effective coordination" of the scientific information activities of the federal government.

As also noted earlier, Reorganization Plan No. 2 of 1962 established the Office of Science and Technology in the Executive Office of the President, and transferred to OST several functions of the National Science Foundation, including functions that would enable OST to assist the President in achieving coordinated federal policies for the promotion of basic research and education in the sciences and functions of evaluating the scientific research programs of the federal agencies.

FINANCES

The method of reporting the financing of science policy planning has been changed so many times that it is difficult to compare this item since the origin of the Foundation. In the first full fiscal year (1952), "development of science policy" accounted for $130,200, and for the "maintenance of information on scientific personnel" $104,000 was expended. In 1962 and 1963, a new and more informative report was made on "science resources planning," budgeted at nearly $1.5 million. In 1964, this subclassification was enlarged to include "long-range policy studies," and the item was entitled "studies of national resources for science and technology." In 1965, the heading of this item was unchanged, but the "long-range policy studies" had been dropped. In 1966, an entirely new section was included—"planning and policy studies," with only two subheads, neither corresponding in wording to those in earlier reports—and over $2 million was expended on this function. Table 17 shows the itemized expenditures for fiscal year 1966.

TABLE 17
NSF Expenditures for Planning and Policy Studies, 1966

Subject of Study	Amount
Scientific and technical manpower resources	
Collection and evaluation of data	$733,817
Policy and program planning	142,168
Subtotal	875,985
Education and research institutions	
Policy and program planning	51,002
Public and private funding of science and technology	
Collection and evaluation of data	222,500
Policy and foreign planning	92,174
Subtotal	314,674
Interactions of science and technology with society	
Policy and program planning	232,972
Science policies and programs, national and foreign	
Policy and program planning	533,968
TOTAL	$2,008,601

SPECIAL STUDIES OF AN URGENT NATURE

In addition to preparing long-range studies for the development of knowledge about the national research effort in science, the Foundation very early decided that special studies of an urgent nature should be undertaken, and they were defined as follows:

These should be on topics of interest from the standpoint of the present emergency, the general welfare or significance to science itself, and should be defined within limits sufficiently narrow to permit completion without undue delay. The aim of such studies would be to determine the extent of research at present being conducted, the degree of Federal support, and the basic research needed to make maximum progress in the special area considered.

The Foundation has engaged in several special studies, some examples of which came early in its career, before 1955. One of these was a review of the medical research programs of the Department of Health, Education, and Welfare, prepared at the request of the department. The Bureau of the Budget requested the Foundation to recommend a uniform policy for payment of indirect costs of research supported by the federal government at universities and colleges. Other policy areas that concerned the Foundation during its early years were minerals research; the future role of the federal government in synthetic rubber research; the support of research by medical students; the role of the Foundation with respect to social science research; a proposal to create a geophysical institute in Hawaii; and the status of high-energy nuclear research.

One important early activity was the systematic study of the national need for scientific installations and facilities. In the Foundation's annual report for 1955, this study is described. The Foundation, acting on the judgment of various advisory bodies composed of specialists, recommended, as a national policy, Government support of large-scale basic scientific facilities.

Subsequent annual reports of the Foundation furnish the details of the accomplishments that have followed from the findings and recommendations of these special studies, particularly of the recommendations in the early study of the need for scientific installations and facilities. (Chapter V contains the account of the Foundation's activities in this area, starting with the establishment of the National Radio Astronomy Observatory and the Kitt Peak National Observatory.)

THE SCIENTIFIC MANPOWER PROGRAM

World War II taught the United States many important lessons about the relationships between science and public policy. One lesson of the utmost importance then and now is the necessity for the government to assume a large measure of responsibility for production of an adequate supply of manpower for science, engineering, and technology. All other plans for developing our capabilities in these areas are dependent, ultimately, on the availability of trained personnel. The government, the universities, and industry are particularly concerned in producing this vitally necessary national resource, and the

National Science Foundation plays an important role in the effort.

Immediately after the end of the war, studies were published emphasizing scientific manpower needs as an important element in our postwar scientific programs. Vannevar Bush, director of the Office of Scientific Research and Development, included one chapter on "The Renewal of our Scientific Talent" in his famous report *Science—The Endless Frontier*. In his proposal for establishment of a national research foundation (the forerunner of the National Science Foundation), he included as one of its major functions the development of scientific talent in American youth by means of scholarships and fellowships.

Shortly after publication of the Bush report, a second important study was published incorporating the findings and recommendations of the President's Scientific Research Board (usually referred to as the Steelman report). It reinforced the recommendations of the Bush report.

As a result of these two studies and of many other strong influences in the same direction, the National Science Register was established in 1950, the same year in which the National Science Foundation was created.

In 1940, the National Resources Planning Board had established the National Roster of Scientific and Specialized Personnel as a register to be used, in case of emergency, for mobilization of manpower. This project underwent several changes of name and was operated by different government agencies. The annual reports of the Foundation from the first (1950–51) to the present (1966) have contained accounts of the Foundation's relationship to the National Science Register. Immediately after the Foundation and the Register were created in 1950, the Register was not placed in the Foundation but was set up as an interim project in the Office of Education of the Federal Security Agency. It was supported initially by the National Security Resources Board, but shortly thereafter the Foundation became financially responsible for it. The collection of information to be included in the Register was commenced immediately. On January 1, 1953, the Register became the responsibility of the Foundation and there it has remained, under the same title.

The Foundation is authorized and directed to "maintain a register of scientific and technical personnel and in other ways provide a clearinghouse for information covering all scientific and technical personnel in the United States, including its territories and possessions."

This function is usually discussed under the general title of the "scientific manpower program," but in carrying out this function the Foundation has performed three different services: operation of the Register as a means of collecting information on individual scientists and assembling available statistics concerning manpower resources; dissemination of analyses and studies of the information so obtained; and preparation of manpower studies on the characteristics of scientific and technical personnel and its utilization, supply, and demand.

The collection of information about individual scientists is conducted in an interesting way. The Foundation, knowing that the different professional societies compiled data concerning their members, established a system based on these records. With some modification of their procedures and with financial assistance from the Foundation, some ten or twelve societies began in 1953 to set up comprehensive registers of their members, on a uniform basis. During 1954–55 information on more than 127,000 individuals was collected, and by 1956–58 the Register contained information about 170,000 scientists.

In 1960, the Committee on Science and Astronautics of the House of Representatives asked the Foundation to prepare a comprehensive report on the Register, its manpower studies, and its plans for the future. This report was not published, but, by the early 1960's, the Foundation had begun to publish many other studies, particularly a series under the title "Scientific Manpower Bulletin." One publication in 1960 was "American Science Manpower, 1960," which summarized the information in the preceding bulletins.

The Foundation recircularizes scientific and technical personnel every two years, to bring the Register up to date. Some 300,000 individual registrants were included in the 1966 listing, and by 1966 the Foundation had also developed a listing of engineers, with 60,000 who had registered in 1964. These persons were requestioned in 1966, with more than forty engineering societies, with 100,000 additional members, also sending questionnaires to their members.

The information on the individuals listed in the Register includes not only the numbers of persons but also what their training is, what technical background they have, their mobility, how much science and science education money is being allocated, who allocates the funds, and how they are being used. Some of the work is done by the Foundation's staff, but much is performed under contract by a number of universities, other government agencies, and nonprofit institutions. The various national scientific and professional organizations, under contract, identify the persons to whom questionnaires should be sent, they mail them out, and they collect them. The Foundation takes this information and edits, compiles, computerizes (the computerization is done under contract with a university center), analyzes, and publishes it. The Census Bureau and the Bureau of Labor Statistics carry out special data collections for the Foundation, using Foundation funds.

At least twenty different federal agencies have responsibilities for information on manpower and education in science and technology. This produces so much information that, clearly, some agency or agencies must coordinate the mass of information. In practice, coordinating functions of one kind or another are performed by the National Science Foundation; in the Executive Office of the President, by the Bureau of the Budget, the Office of Science and Technology, the Federal Council for Science and Technology, and the President's Committee on Manpower, established in 1964; and by the Department of Labor. To assist in this function, the Foundation's Advisory Panel for Manpower and Education Studies Programs, made up of representatives from eleven different agencies, engages in data collection and analysis.

There is no question as to the values of maintaining the Register and of preparing analyses of other information concerning scientific personnel. As scientific and technological development, both public and private, continues to expand, there is recognition that "budgeting" to support it must include manpower as well as funds. The adjustment of available manpower, present and prospective, to the requirements for it, present and prospective, is a matter of major importance. Obviously, the collection, analysis, and coordination of relevant data are the indispensable bases for policy decisions.

STUDIES OF PUBLIC AND PRIVATE FUNDING OF SCIENCE

The Foundation conducts or supports many serial and periodic studies dealing with the financing of scientific activities.

Probably the best known and most widely used of these publications is the annual government-wide "Federal Funds for Research, Development, and Other Scientific Activities." Volume XVI covers fiscal years 1966, 1967, and 1968. Since the series has been continuous since 1953 it presents, to quote the foreword of the fifteenth edition:

> . . . a body of systematic statistical information on the size and scope of Federal spending for scientific activities, to indicate the methods by which these funds are spent, and to show important trends in major spending areas. The statistics are designed to contribute to understanding the current situation and to be useful in formulating science policy and plans from the point of view both of the Federal Government and of the Nation as a whole.
>
> Federal participation in scientific research and development is not a single and separate entity, easy to measure and describe. It springs from many sources within different agencies to help meet the needs in the discharge of their various missions, and its effectiveness for this purpose must be judged primarily in terms of agency goals. However, the national interest also

requires that Federal investment in research and development and other scientific activities be summarized in broad totals, cutting across agency lines, to provide a measure of the impact of Federal programs on national scientific resources.

In 1963, the Foundation published its first report on the geographical distribution of federal funds for research and development, and the second report was published in 1967. Those who contribute to the making of national scientific policy have shown a growing interest in the subject because, with the increased funds for these purposes, far-reaching effects on the economy have resulted, and different sections of the country understandably wish to participate in the benefits. The two Foundation reports have shown the state-by-state distribution of funds by the major federal research and development agencies and by the various performers within the states.

A second type of financial study prepared by the Foundation includes reports on basic and applied research and development in industry. Annually, since 1953, the Foundation has supported a survey performed by the Bureau of the Census, describing research and development conducted by industry and by non-academic institutions.

In addition to reports on the financing of industrial research and development, and reports on federal government funds for scientific research, the Foundation has more recently become heavily involved in reporting on federal funding for academic institutions. The President issued a directive on September 13, 1965, calling for support for research on this subject, and the Federal Council for Science and Technology established the Committee on Academic Science and Engineering (CASE) with the director of the National Science Foundation as its chairman and with NSF staff support. One result was establishment of the first government-wide compatible system for reporting federal support for universities and colleges on an institution-by-institution basis. It covers funds for research and development, research and development plant, institutional support, other science-related activities, and nonscience activities. Its first report was published in October, 1966, and work has continued on further analysis, and on preparation of a revised reporting system, which will yield a wide variety of factual information. The Foundation led a cooperative effort in the development of a single institutional directory to facilitate storage and retrieval of all types of information relating to all institutions of higher education in the United States.

STUDIES OF EDUCATIONAL AND RESEARCH INSTITUTIONS

In addition to reporting on the federal funds for research and development in universities, colleges, and other research institutions, the Foundation conducts other types of research concerning these agencies. An indication of the present nature of these studies was given in the Foundation's annual report for 1966, which listed surveys conducted and analyses prepared on the following subjects:

1. college freshmen, graduates, graduate students, and science doctorates;
2. a continuation of studies on the career progress of science graduates;
3. analyses of recently acquired information concerning doctoral education in the sciences;
4. three studies of university growth and development, previously started, with the objective of developing mathematical models of university cost structure, physical facilities, faculty, student body, and other factors;
5. beginning of a two-year sponsored study of "The Outlook for Higher Education in 1980";
6. a survey of science activities in nonacademic, nonprofit institutions;
7. several major surveys and analyses of industrial research and development;
8. arrangements for improving exchange of policy and program information with large research-oriented industrial corporations and with large philanthropic foundations; and
9. the industrial adoption of new technological advances.

STUDIES OF SCIENCE POLICIES AND PROGRAMS, NATIONAL AND FOREIGN

A considerable amount of the funds expended for studies of science policies is transferred by the Foundation for support of the Committee on Science and Public Policy (COSPUP) of the National Academy of Sciences. Four major reports, issued in 1966, were: *Chemistry: Opportunities and Needs; Digital Computer Needs in Universities and Colleges; Physics; Survey and Outlook;* and *The Plant Sciences: Now and in the Coming Decade.* Two new surveys covering the mathematical and life sciences were initiated that year, and a study of the behavioral and social sciences was continued. Other analytical studies, both domestic and foreign, were devoted to (1) policy-oriented subjects, such as the mechanisms used by the federal government to support scientific research in universities; (2) patterns of federal expenditures for academic science; (3) resource allocation processes and decision points in the federal government; (4) criteria for resource allocation, with special attention to the institutional and geographic distribution of federal funds in relation to scientific activities and manpower; (5) a study of U.S. science policy prepared for UNESCO's Science Policy Division; (6) provision of data to the Organization for Economic Development (OECD) for the International Statistical Year, and for OECD's study of the international migration of scientists and engineers; and (7) completion or publication of *Scientific and Engineering Manpower in Communist China; Women in the Soviet Economy;* and *Scientific Manpower in the Arab Countries.*

Attention is called to one of the annual publications of the Foundation, *Current Projects on Economic and Social Implications of Science and Technology,* which contains summaries of university-based research in the broad area of its title and in the related areas of scientific manpower, and the history and philosophy of science. This publication meets an increasing demand for better understanding of the social and economic effects of advances in science and technology.

XI

NSF Relationships with Other Executive Branch Agencies

By now, the reader has some idea of the complexities surrounding the Foundation's relationships with the President, with the different science agencies and the Bureau of the Budget in the Executive Office of the President, and with the several departments and agencies carrying out government-wide scientific activities. The Foundation's program activities are full of examples of interrelationships—in carrying out science education programs, in the area of international science activities, and so on. The legal authority for these activities has been cited, but there are several other relevant provisions of the National Science Foundation Act shaping NSF relationships within the U.S. government.

Under Section 1870 (c), at the request of the Secretary of Defense, the Foundation has the authority to enter into contracts or other arrangements for carrying on, by organizations or individuals in the United States or in foreign countries, of specific scientific research activities in connection with matters relating to the national defense. Section 1873(h) specifies that the research funds of other government departments and agencies may be transferred, with the approval of the head of the department or agency, to the Foundation for use consistent with the purpose for which the funds were provided. The section of the act dealing with security provisions describes the relationships between the NSF and the Atomic Energy Commission and the Department of Defense, stating that the Foundation shall not support any research or development activity in the field of nuclear energy, nor exercise any authority granted to NSF in connection with acquisition of property without having first obtained the concurrence of the AEC that such activity will not adversely affect the common defense and security. Provisions of the Atomic Energy Act of 1946 with regard to control of restricted data and security clearance of individuals to be given access to it are applicable to the Foundation.

Additional legal provisions found in statutes not dealing with the Foundation, include the following: (1) the director of the Foundation, or his designee, is included in the membership of the Advisory Committee on Weather Control; the assistant director of Biological and Medical Sciences of the Foundation is a member of the Board of Regents of the National Library of Medicine; the Librarian of Congress, in consultation with the Foundation, is given certain functions concerning the use of foreign currencies and foreign publications; a representative of the Foundation is included in the membership of the Advisory Committee on Graduate Education in the Office of Education; the Federal Council on the Arts and Humanities includes the director of the Foundation as a member.

Representatives of the Foundation are also included in many similar interdepartmental committees established by Executive Order of the President and by less formal means.

The President and the NSF

Five Presidents have exercised direct influence on the establishment and development of the National Science Foundation over the years. Under Franklin D. Roosevelt, the most important events were the establishment of the Office of Scientific Research and Development (OSRD), a forerunner of the NSF; and the appointment of the committee, headed by Vannevar Bush, which reported in 1945 to President Truman.

Harry S Truman received the Bush committee report containing a recommendation for a body like the NSF; appointed the President's Scientific Research Board (chairman, John R.

Steelman), which also recommended a body like the NSF; supported and signed the National Science Foundation Act of 1950; and created the Interdepartmental Committee on Scientific Research and Development (1947), supported by the NSF after 1951, and abolished in 1959 when the Federal Council for Science and Technology was established.

Dwight D. Eisenhower issued Executive Order 10521 on March 17, 1954. It dealt with the administration of research by the NSF. It was modified by his Executive Order 10807 on March 13, 1959, which established the Federal Council on Science and Technology (FCST), including the director of NSF as a member. In 1957, President Eisenhower created the post of Special Assistant for Science and Technology, which has been maintained to the present. He also transferred the Science Advisory Committee of the Office of Defense Mobilization to the office of the President, where it still exists, now known as the President's Science Advisory Committee (PSAC).

John F. Kennedy's Reorganization Plan No. 2 of 1962 established the Office of Science and Technology (OST) and altered the powers of the Foundation in important respects. It was followed by Lyndon B. Johnson's Reorganization Plan No. 5 of 1965, July 27, 1965, relating to the committees of the Foundation and to the Director's power to delegate authority.

Under the National Science Foundation Act of 1950, the President has certain functions in relation to the Foundation. The twenty-four members of the National Science Board are appointed by the President by and with the advice and consent of the Senate. The President is requested to give due consideration to recommendations from the National Academy of Sciences and other organizations. The Director of the Foundation is appointed by the President by and with the advice and consent of the Senate and serves for six years unless he is sooner removed by the President. The award of the National Medal of Science by the President is made on the basis of recommendations by the Foundation and other relevant information.

Executive Order 10807, which established the Federal Council for Science and Technology, provided that the Foundation shall recommend to the President policies for the promotion of basic research and education in the sciences, including policies with respect to furnishing guidance toward defining the responsibilities of the federal government in the conduct and support of basic scientific research.

It should be noted that the President's influence over scientific research is by no means exercised entirely through such formal actions and legal provisions as those just described. Through the messages he writes when he transmits the Foundation's and other agencies' annual reports to Congress, the messages he sends to many meetings of scientific organizations conveying his support, through his determination of the amounts of money for the annual budgets of the federal science agencies, which he makes in his annual recommendations to Congress, through his memoranda and directives to the departments and agencies, and in many other statements and actions he exerts great additional leverage. A few examples may be cited. In November, 1957, President Eisenhower made two major addresses to the nation—"Science in National Security" and "Our Future Security"—in which he stressed the importance of science and emphasized the need to give higher priority to scientific education and to basic research. A more recent instance is President Johnson's statement in the letter he sent to Congress on April 6, 1967, when he transmitted the 1966 annual report of the Foundation. He wrote that the NSF, "is entrusted, *more than any other single national institution,* with the responsibility to expand our reservoir of scientific knowledge through research, and to promote excellence in our scientific education." (Emphasis added.)

THE EXECUTIVE OFFICE OF THE PRESIDENT

The President works through a special assistant and several agencies in the Executive Office. Of all departments and agencies of the executive branch of the federal government, the one that is closest to the President is, of course, his own staff agency—the Executive Office of the President. Several of its subdivisions have important responsibilities in connection with the science activities of the government. For example, there is the Special Presidential Assistant for Science and Technology in the White House Office. Donald F. Hornig, who held the position at the time this book was written, also served as chairman of the President's Science Advisory Committee (PSAC), chairman of the Federal Council for Science and Technology (FCST), and director of the Office of Science and Technology (OST), and his advice was based on the coordinated contributions of these top-level bodies. Hornig's predecessors in the position of Presidential science adviser were James R. Killian, Jr., the president of the Massachusetts Institute of Technology, who held office from 1959 to 1961, and Jerome B. Wiesner, also from M.I.T.

The President's Science Advisory Committee (PSAC) is made up of the Special Assistant for Science and Technology and distinguished scientists and engineers, drawn from the universities, industry, and other parts of the scientific community. They are appointed by the President and are concerned with major scientific and technological issues.

The function of the Federal Council for Science and Technology (FCST) is to promote closer cooperation among federal departments and agencies, and to coordinate the total federal effort in science and technology. The Special Assistant to the President is chairman, and the members are top policy-level representatives from each of the federal agencies involved in science and technology. In November, 1967, the President enlarged the membership. The Council now has twelve members, including the director of the National Science Foundation, and it operates largely through a series of interagency committees.

The Office of Science and Technology (OST) was created by Reorganization Plan No. 2 of 1962, as the most recent element of the federal superstructure for science. The Special Assistant is its director, and the OST is generally responsible for coordination of science and technology functions, having taken over from the National Science Foundation a large part of its responsibilities for development of national policies for science and evaluation of the scientific research programs of the government agencies. The OST provides staff assistance for the Special Assistant, the PSAC, and the FCST.

Still another part of the scientific roster in the Executive Office of the President is the National Council on Marine Resources and Engineering, which was created in the Sea Grant Colleges and Marine Science Development Act of 1966. The Vice President of the United States is the chairman and the members are the secretaries of State, the Navy, the Interior, Commerce, Transportation and Health, Education, and Welfare, the chairman of the Atomic Energy Commission, and the director of the National Science Foundation. The President may appoint additional officers as he deems advisable. The Council advises and assists the President in carrying out his duties under the act, including the development, encouragement and maintenance of a coordinated, comprehensive, and long-range program in marine science. The Sea Grant College and Program Act of 1966 is administered by the National Science Foundation, and as the President may request, seeks advice from the National Council on Marine Resources and Engineering Development.

The most important relations of the Foundation to this whole superstructure appear to be with the Office of Science and Technology. Three special relationships were defined in House Report 1236 (1966):

> *Collection of basic data.* The Foundation has a central responsibility to provide basic data on science resources, on expenditures for research and development, and on scientific manpower. The data acquisition and analysis capabilities of the Foundation are utilized by the OST as a basis for the development of national science policies.
>
> *Special assignments.* The Foundation can serve either as an executive agent or a delegated agent of the OST in taking the lead in certain assignments of broad importance. For example, the OST requested the Foundation to develop an interagency

assessment of and reaction to the recent report of the National Academy of Sciences on needs in ground based astronomy.

Advice on science policy. According to Dr. Hornig, the Foundation is a "particularly valuable source of advice" to the OST on science policies that merit consideration for Government-wide application.

Dr. Hornig also identified another relationship between the Foundation and the OST, similar to that of the Executive Office with other departments and agencies. *The OST reviews and examines the programs of the Foundation in the same way it looks at those of other agencies.* Because of the limited OST staff, this examination is highly selective and concentrates on items of major importance. It is concerned mainly with the directions in which the programs are tending, the opportunities that may be neglected, and major budgetary issues.

The Foundation also, of course, like all other executive branch departments and agencies, has a close and important relationship with the Bureau of the Budget. William D. Carey, who at the time was assistant director of the Bureau, in an article in *Scientific Research* (July, 1967), wrote that "the breadth of the Bureau's involvement in science is awesome," and he gave examples of science matters on which it has had to take a position in recent years. These matters involved science legislation, choosing to spend or not to spend, organization and management, and research-grant management. His description of the budget cycle through which the Foundation must progress, as do the other executive branch departments and agencies, included these paragraphs:

Many an R&D project falls during this period—most often to a challenge from the Bureau alone but, in some cases, to the combined opposition of the Bureau and Hornig's office. Only in those few cases when an agency decides to fight is the President asked to involve himself.

When issues have to go to the President, it's the Bureau's job to define the problem—to spell out the issues, the public-policy implications, the alternative approaches, the costs of deferring the decision and the dollar costs of all of these, if they can be measured or estimated.

We're concerned with the merits of the projects but we don't have the scientific judgment—this is where Hornig and his people come in. We're more concerned with the rationality of the review. Have the right questions been asked? Has a full analysis been made?

Our job is to make sure the thing has gone through all the main hurdles and we may throw in one or two more just to make the guy jump a little. . . . Our role is to be part of the process of the translation from the scientific to the lay judgment because, in the final analysis, it goes to the President and the Congress, who act for the layman.

A sweeping reorganization of the BOB became effective in 1968, with the creation of six broad program divisions. One is the Science, Technology, and Economic Division to review the budgets of the National Science Foundation, the Atomic Energy Commission, the National Aeronautics and Space Administration, the Department of Transportation, the Small Business Administration, and some regulatory agencies. One important change that this reorganization effects is separation of the Foundation and the Office of Education, which formerly fell into one division.

The National Science Foundation is bound into the science and technology policy-making functions of the executive branch through its formal membership in these various agencies of the Executive Office of the President. Although the founders of NSF and its early supporters intended the Foundation to be *the* science policy-making body, the continual development has been to raise this function beyond the level of any one department or agency to the only place where there is strong enough over-all authority to deal with it—that is, to the Office of the President. There, the Foundation *as one among equals* participates in advising the President, developing science policy, and reviewing, coordinating, and supervising the science and technology programs of the departments and agencies. (With the wisdom of hindsight, it might be added, such a development appears to have been inevitable.)

From the published record it is difficult to determine the

precise means by which a dozen or so major departments and agencies managed to cooperate with each other in such a way as to produce a coordinated program for a particular activity. That they do so cooperate is repeatedly stated by their representatives, and it must be assumed that they speak fact, because it can scarcely be imagined that any activity could long be carried out if each department pursued an independent course. Of course, the several agencies in the Executive Office of the President are, to a large extent, occupied in this very task of coordinating the related programs of several different departments and agencies. In any case, it is not difficult to single out the programs that need to be coordinated. The special analyses the Bureau of the Budget attaches to the President's annual budget describes among other things, "selected government-wide scientific activities." The special analyses for fiscal 1968 described six, in all of which the National Science Foundation was a participant: (1) atmospheric sciences (meteorology, aeronomy, planetary atmospheres), (2) medical research, (3) marine science and technology, (4) space programs, (5) water research, (6) science information.

OCEANOGRAPHY GOVERNMENT-WIDE

The support of research in marine science and technology, or oceanography, by the federal government is distributed among twenty or more federal departments and agencies in what D. S. Greenberg has referred to as "orchestrated anarchy." The Interagency Committee on Oceanography in the Executive Office of the President was first charged with the "orchestration" of a program costing more than $300 million per year, but Congress has found it increasingly difficult to understand this program—if, indeed, it can properly be called a program. A solution was proposed in a bill (S.944) introduced in the first session (1965) of the Eighty-ninth Congress, which was passed in the second session (1966) as Public Law 89-454, the Marine Research and Development Act of 1966.

The National Science Foundation's major part in the work

resulting from the new law can be demonstrated by a look at Table 18, which shows the actual obligations for fiscal year 1966 of the eleven departments and agencies supporting principal elements of the oceanography program that year. The same table contained estimates for 1967 totaling $409 million and for 1968 totaling $462 million, but it is difficult to compare any of these amounts with those for earlier periods, which included only activities reported as "oceanography." The current activities include oceanography as previously defined, plus expanded coverage of areas such as the development of fisheries, assessment of marine mineral and energy resources, and military technology. For example, the National Sea Grant College and Program Act of 1966 provided new activities under the jurisdiction of the National Science Foundation.

For many years, the National Science Foundation has supported research in oceanography, not as a separate entity, but as an integral part of the various existing programs. There have been hundreds of individual research projects in biological oceanography and physical oceanography. The Foundation has provided assistance for construction of research

TABLE 18
Financial Obligations for Oceanographic Research, 1966
(in Millions of Dollars)

Department or Agency	Amount
Commerce	$25.0
Defense	174.9
Health, Education, and Welfare	5.4
Interior	56.5
State	5.0
Transportation	8.1
Agency for International Development	0.1
Atomic Energy Commission	8.3
National Aeronautics and Space Administration	0.9
National Science Foundation	47.7
Smithsonian Institution	1.5
TOTAL	$333.4

vessels, and has made grants to various institutions for building shore facilities, including research laboratory buildings. Two of the national research programs administered by the Foundation—the U.S. Antarctic Research Program and the U.S. portion of the International Indian Ocean Expedition—contain large elements of oceanographic research. (Project Mohole, terminated in 1966, was another part of the Foundation's oceanography program.) Some half dozen of its divisions administer these different programs. In fiscal year 1966, they spent nearly $30 million on oceanography.

WEATHER MODIFICATION GOVERNMENT-WIDE

The National Science Foundation is only one of the several federal departments and agencies conducting research programs in "artificially produced changes in the composition, behavior, and dynamics of the atmosphere"—which is one definition of weather modification. The principal ones are the departments of the Interior, Commerce, and Defense (Army, Navy, Air Force), but eight different agencies support fifty different projects. As a result, the problem of coordination of their various programs has become more urgent as the size and scope of these programs have increased. No one of the departments and agencies is designated by law to be the coordinating mechanism. The Foundation is authorized "to initiate and support a program of study, research, and evaluation in the field of weather modification," and presumably acting under this power it has, in practice, performed some coordinating functions. But the structure of coordination includes also the Interdepartmental Committee on Atmospheric Sciences of the Federal Council for Science and Technology, in the Office of Science and Technology in the Executive Office of the President; the Advisory Panel for Weather Modification of the NSF; the Interagency Committee on International Meteorological Programs; and the Panel on Weather and Climate Modification, Committee on Atmospheric Sciences, National Academy of Sciences. Once a year, the NSF calls a two-day conference of the working-level scientists in all federal agencies with weather modification programs.

The relative size of the various weather modification programs is indicated by their funding for fiscal year 1966, which is shown in Table 19.

TABLE 19
Funding of Weather Modification Programs, 1966

Agency	Amount
Department of the Interior	$2,905,500
National Science Foundation	2,001,782
Navy	777,100
Army	285,000
Air Force	205,000
Department of Commerce	650,000
National Aeronautics and Space Administration	70,000
TOTAL	$7,034,382

The NSF and the Department of Commerce, through its Environmental Science Services Administration (ESSA), carry on programs of research in many different aspects of weather modification but other agencies are concerned primarily with one or a few types with close, "mission-oriented" relationships to their major functions. For example, NASA, in 1966, worked principally on fog dissipation.

SCIENCE EDUCATION GOVERNMENT-WIDE

Science education is probably the single field of activity in which the largest number of federal agencies operates. It is not easy to describe all of these programs, conducted by some twenty different agencies, let alone sift out their relationships to the National Science Foundation programs discussed in Chapter VI. Indeed, it is not even possible to get statistical information on the amounts spent on science education by all of these agencies, partly because such sums may be listed under other headings, or grouped with nonscientific, but related activities. Thus, of the more than $2.3 billion expended by eight reporting departments and agencies, according to figures released by the NSF in 1966, some $1.8 billion were used for academic science, with the remaining $543 million for "other educational activities" (chiefly, the program of the Office of Education for construction and initial equipping of undergraduate facilities).

As these enormous sums continue to be spent every year, the possibilities for duplication and conflict can be imagined. One would certainly conclude that some mechanism for coordination must exist. There are, in fact, several points of coordination which may be mentioned, without going into the details of their operation.

Frequently, statutory boards, with members from related areas, and ad hoc committees are appointed with multiagency membership. And, as already noted, in the Executive Office of the President, the Bureau of the Budget, the Science Adviser to the President, the Office of Science and Technology, and the Federal Council for Science and Technology have the opportunity at the highest level to coordinate science activities, including the different science education programs. But perhaps the best results come from the close, informal contacts between officials responsible for administering separate programs in areas of joint responsibility. Also, the universities themselves in planning the financing of their science programs must prepare carefully coordinated programs before they apply for federal support.

In its 1965 annual report, the Foundation included a brief section explaining the complementary functions of the Office of Education and the Foundation. This is a good example of cooperation in a situation where opportunities for coordination are particularly significant, because these two agencies are most centrally and directly involved in support of federal educational activities—the Foundation for science education alone, and the Office of Education for education in general. Under the Higher Education Facilities Act of 1963, the Office of Education provides grants and loans for both graduate and undergraduate facilities in colleges and universities, for the purpose of developing new centers of excellence in graduate studies to increase the number of highly qualified people needed in industry, government, teaching, and research. This facilities program complements the NSF program, which is primarily concerned with research facilities alone. Coordination between the two agencies is effected by statutory provision for NSF memberships on the Office of Education committee advising on graduate facilities grants. Other areas of shared responsibility are the improvement of the qualifications of elementary and secondary school teachers; graduate fellowship programs; and improvement of education through curriculum improvement projects. Close coordination in such projects is effected in three ways: (1) an NSF staff member serves on the OE curriculum improvement review panel; (2) NSF and OE members sometimes conduct joint site visits to investigate the research potential of proposed project locations; and (3) the two agencies jointly review and fund proposals that relate to both agencies.

A second example of coordination that seems to be successful is the Federal Council on Science and Technology's Committee on Academic Science and Engineering (CASE). In includes representatives of all major federal agencies that support scientific research and education at academic institutions, with the director of the National Science Foundation as chairman. During its first year, CASE initiated several important coordinating actions among these agencies, many of which are now in operation. In its 1966 annual report, the NSF said:

> It is hoped that these and other projects, together with concerted actions resulting from discussions within the Committee itself, can go far toward alleviating many of the difficulties now encountered by academic institutions in dealing with the Federal Government as a result of differing policies and administrative practices among the various agencies.

XII

The Foundation and Congress

As is the case with all the executive branch departments and agencies, the National Science Foundation was created by Congress. Congress enacts legislation every year providing funds for each of them, and it enacts laws prescribing their functions and, in many cases, the details of their organizations. This chapter will describe the relationships between Congress and a single agency, the National Science Foundation, which it created in 1950. The first section contains a general discussion of the nature of this relationship; the second section, in order to give a concrete illustration of this relationship in operation, describes the actions of one session of Congress (the Eighty-ninth Congress, second session, in 1966) with respect to the Foundation; the third section describes briefly the changes incorporated in Public Law 90-407, enacted in 1968.

The relationship with the National Science Foundation is a single part—and by no means the largest—of the relationship of Congress to national science policy. This fact makes it necessary to give some preliminary attention to the broader subject as background.

Congress and National Science Policy

The Committee on Science and Astronautics of the House of Representatives, in its report, "The National Science Foundation: Its Present and Future," included a chapter entitled "The Congressional View," which, in brief space, discussed

Congress and national science policy. The following quotation is taken from this source:

> Within a single generation, science and technology have so permeated our society and economy that there remains scarcely a part of the Federal Government not profoundly influenced and affected by Federal research and development. With this change has come a congressional involvement with science that has increased markedly from year to year. Today almost every committee of both the House and the Senate is concerned with science and technology, albeit in varying degrees. Legislative committees whose interests are *primarily* scientific include the House Committee on Science and Astronautics, the Senate Committee on Aeronautical and Space Sciences, and the Joint Committee on Atomic Energy. A quick look at the jurisdictions of other committees reveals scientific and technological interests of the Joint Committee on Economics; the House Committees on Agriculture, Armed Services, Education and Labor, Foreign Affairs, Government Operations, Interstate and Foreign Commerce, Judiciary, Merchant Marine and Fisheries, and Post Office and Civil Service; and the Senate Committees on Agriculture and Forestry, Armed Services, Commerce, Foreign Relations, Government Operations, Judiciary, and Labor and Public Welfare. These scientific interests generally are a part, not the whole, of the committees' jurisdictions. Furthermore, most of the committees confine themselves to after-the-fact reviews. Except for those committees which participate in advance planning through exercising authorization functions, most others have confined themselves largely to ad hoc investigations of specific aspects of Federal research and development which limit their opportunities to lead in shaping national science policies. At present, the programs of the Atomic Energy Commission; the National Aeronautics and Space Administration; the Department of Defense for procurement of aircraft, missiles, and ships, and for research and development; the Arms Control and Disarmament Agency and foreign aid require annual authorization.

The Appropriations Committees of the House and the Senate have a special sort of role and their influence and impact is of a different kind. They are strategically placed to influence important aspects of policies and programs for science and also in prescribing specific limitations as well.

In the Senate, the continuing interest of the Government Operations Committee in science information is well known, as is also its interest in a Commission on Science and Technology. It was the Subcommittee on National Policy Machinery of that Committee which is credited with the suggestions for reorganizing scientific activities in the Executive Office which resulted in the establishment of the Office of Science and Technology. . . . The Committee on Government Operations announced appointment of a Special Subcommittee on Government Research to conduct studies and hearings into the operations of Federal research and development programs.

In the Senate also, the Select Committee on Small Business held extensive hearings on the role and effect of technology in the nation's economy during 1963. Recently, during May and June 1965, the Employment and Manpower Subcommittee of the Senate Labor and Public Welfare Committee held hearings on the impact on national scientific and technical manpower of Federal research and development policies.

Recommendations from congressional studies that Congress acquire its own scientific staff led to the establishment of a Science Policy Research Division within the Legislative Reference Service of the Library of Congress.

The fragmentation of Federal science among the Committees of Congress poses a problem of congressional management of its own affairs so that it can give better attention to the whole of Federal scientific activities. Despite this fragmentation, members and committees of Congress are beginning to ask probing questions about the purposes and policies of Federal science. The intention is not so much to take over the policy initiative for scientific research as it is to assure that someone within the executive branch should seize the initiative and do it well and thoroughly.

CONGRESSIONAL POLICY TOWARD THE FOUNDATION

As might be expected, there are many published treatments of the subject of Congress and the NSF. David Allison in *International Science and Technology* (April, 1966), mentioned the early hostility of a suspicious Congress which made "a deadly budget cut" in the first very modest request for an appropriation, saying:

> The House of Representatives chose to give it nothing, and voted so. Only the intervention of the Senate, and Warren Magnuson, of the state of Washington, saved the young agency from more years in oblivion.
>
> Today, it is a different story. There is still controversy, still stinging criticism of this agency which has tried so hard these many years to stay away from controversy, but now the critics complain that the Foundation does too little, that it is not aggressive enough, that it is not doing more for the colleges. And who are the critics? The congressmen are perhaps the loudest and most thoughtful of them. The congressmen! Times have changed.

The change in congressional views has been drastic, but it has not meant that members have turned to unbounded generosity. Nor has Congress refrained from scoffing at some of the research projects that scientists have wanted to perform and the Foundation has wanted to finance. But, Allison continued:

> . . . the Congress of today views the Foundation as a permanent part of the governmental establishment. It views the support of science, including science education, as a national commitment. And that is the drastic change. This year, for instance, the Congress will appropriate some $500 million to the Foundation. This is 2,000 times the amount it allocated in that first year of NSF's existence, and 130 times the allocation of the second year. In fact, the Congress will allocate more money to NSF during this next year than it allocated *in toto* during the first ten years of the Foundation's life.

During its short history, according to Allison, the Foundation has acquired more friends than enemies among the membership of Congress. He mentioned particularly, in addition to Senator Warren G. Magnuson (Washington), former Senator Leverett Saltonstall (Massachusetts) and former Representative Albert Thomas, who for many years was chairman of the Subcommittee on Independent Offices of the House Committee on Appropriations, which reviewed the Foundation's annual budget. He also singled out Emilio Q. Daddario, who chaired a subcommittee of the House Committee on Science and Astronautics, which held extensive hearings on the NSF during consideration of proposed new legislation in 1966:

> Like most congressmen, Daddario does not have a technical background. He practiced law in Hartford before being elected to the House, in 1958. Nonetheless, the inquiry of Daddario and his subcommittee—the Subcommittee on Science, Research, and Development, which performed its investigation last summer—was marked with excellence as few congressional investigations in memory.

Allison's article continued with a description of the inquiry which was conducted by Daddario's subcommittee, whose "tough, thorough, intelligent investigation, conducted in the spirit of a friendly dialogue" had made thorough preparation for the hearings; the chairman, Representative Daddario, and his colleagues, Allison said, asked questions that were "often superior to the answers they evoked" and showed a "deeper understanding of the place of science in our society."

House Report 1236, cited above for its excellent description of the relation of Congress to science policy in general, contained the following similarly clear statement on legislative oversight of the National Science Foundation:

> Through the first 15 years of its history, the Foundation has received attention of several committees of the Congress. In the House, the Committee on Interstate and Foreign Commerce had jurisdiction for the NSF until 1958 when this responsibility was assumed by the House Committee on Science and Astronautics. The establishment of this Subcommittee on Science, Research, and Development in 1963 provided the base for the present review of the Foundation. In the Senate, the Committee on Labor and Public Welfare has had continuing jurisdiction.
>
> As an indication of the range of total congressional interest in the Foundation, the NSF Director has appeared before at least nine committees of the House, eight of the Senate, and two congressional joint committees. The subjects of these hearings have

ranged from NSF organization to radioactive fallout and its effect upon man.

The published record of the Independent Offices appropriations subcommittee hearings show the scrutiny of NSF programs and activities by the Appropriations Committees of each House. These hearings reveal matters of concern to the Congress such as management of research programs, funding of expensive facilities and concentration of research funds and fellowship grants. While the Appropriations Subcommittees do not determine what research and development should be done by agencies appearing before them, they can and do question and change budget allocations for specific programs.

The four subcommittees that had jurisdiction over the Foundation in the Eighty-ninth and Ninetieth Congresses were the following:

House of Representatives
  Committee on Appropriations:
    Subcommittee on Independent Offices—
      Chairman, Representative Joe L. Evins (Tennessee)
    Committee on Science and Astronautics:
    Subcommittee on Science, Research, and Development
      —Chairman, Emilio Q. Daddario (Connecticut)
Senate
  Committee on Appropriations:
    Subcommittee on Independent Offices—
      Chairman, Warren G. Magnuson (Washington)
    Committee on Labor and Public Welfare—
      Chairman, Lister B. Hill (Alabama). Usually NSF
      bills are sent to the Subcommittee on Education—
      Chairman, Wayne Morse (Oregon)

Congress has had under consideration, since early 1965, the whole subject of the jurisdiction of the committees. The Joint Committee on the Organization of Congress reported in July, 1966 a plan containing provisions which related directly to jurisdiction over the affairs of the Foundation. The general purpose was to reorganize certain committees and to distribute functions in such a way that, in the Senate and in the House, there would be parallel committees on science and astronautics with identical functions, including supervision of the Foundation. Reaction to these proposals produced objections to the effort to consolidate committee jurisdiction over science and technology. The principal objection was that they would break the connection between scientific activities and the functions of the agencies in which they are presently located. The Chairman of the Senate Commerce Committee, Warren G. Magnuson (Washington), expressed this judgment especially strongly. However, the recommendations of the Joint Committee on the Organization of Congress were not acted on by Congress in the Eighty-ninth and the Ninetieth Congresses.

THE FOUNDATION AND THE SECOND SESSION OF THE EIGHTY-NINTH CONGRESS

In order that one may really appreciate the relationships between the Foundation and the Congress, it is useful to study them in a concrete situation. A history of the subject from 1945, when Congress first considered establishment of the Foundation, to the present would show some sessions in which very important matters were considered and many in which the only important action was that taken on the Foundation's annual budget. The second session of the Eighty-ninth Congress in 1966 furnishes a useful example and the remainder of this section contains an account of legislation enacted and proposed legislation, relating both directly and indirectly to the Foundation.

Briefly, the following events occurred. The President transmitted to the Congress the budget of the U.S. government for the fiscal year ending June 30, 1967. The budget for the National Science Foundation was considered by the subcommittees and then by the full committees on Appropriations of the Senate and the House. The records of their hearings were published, although the hearings were not open to the public. These committees reported the appropriation bill for fiscal year 1967, containing the NSF appropriation (H.R. 14921), which was enacted as Public Law 89-555, including "sundry independent executive bureaus, boards, commissions, corporations, agencies, offices, and the Department of Housing and Urban Development." It is usually referred to as the Independent Offices Appropriation Act, 1967.

Early in the session, two important committee reports were published. In 1965, the Subcommittee on Science, Research and Development of the House Committee on Science and Astronautics had held very extensive hearings which constituted a public review of the Foundation. These hearings were open to the public and the records were published as *The National Science Foundation; a General Review of Its First 15 Years* (89th Cong., 2d Sess., House Report 1219. Washington: U.S. Gov't. Printing Office, 1966) and *The National Science Foundation; Its Present and Future* (89th Cong., 2d Sess., House Report 1236. Washington, U.S. Gov't. Printing Office, 1966). The National Science Foundation's annual report for 1965 was sent to the Congress.

In addition to the appropriation act described above, Congress passed one more act directly involving the Foundation— Public Law 89-688, "The National Sea Grant College and Program Act of 1966" (H.R. 16559).

The Marine Resources and Development Act of 1966 (Public Law 89-454) involved the Foundation in two ways: its subject was oceanography, in which federal activity the Foundation has an important part, and the National Council established by the law included among its members the director of NSF.

The House of Representatives passed H.R. 14838, providing for changes in the organization and operation of the National Science Foundation. An identical bill (S. 3465) was referred to the Senate Committee on Labor and Public Welfare. This Committee did not hold hearings nor take action on either measure.

The Senate passed S. 2916, which provided for coordination of the numerous weather research and control programs, including that of the NSF. This and H.R. 14838 contained a repeal of the Foundation's program of initiation and support of a program of study, research, and evaluation. No action was taken on S. 2916 in the House, and no action on H.R. 14838 in the Senate.

Several bills in the House (H. Res. 780, 808, 809, 810, and 904) and two in the Senate, each with several cosponsors (S. Res. 231 and 250), contained the request for the National Science Foundation to transmit to Congress its recommendations for changes in the law, or in its administration, to provide for a more equitable distribution of research funds to universities, on a geographical basis. No hearings on these bills were held, and no action was taken. Section 3(e) of H.R. 14838 contained provision for prevention of undue geographical distribution. S. Res. 218 was passed by the Senate, authorizing the Senate Committee on Government Operations to make studies, including the equitable distribution of research and development contracts (Section 1(3)).

H.R. 12242 provided an amendment to the National Science Foundation Act requiring prior authorization by Congress before any appropriation could be made to the Foundation. No hearings were held and no action was taken.

A bill (H.R. 13786) was introduced providing for a national program of institutional grants to the colleges and universities of the United States, to advance science and promote the education of scientists. The program was to be administered by the National Science Foundation. No action was taken on this bill.

Several measures not relating specifically to the Foundation but of indirect interest included: the International Education Act of 1966 (Public Law 89-698); the proposed International Brain Drain Act of 1966, introduced in the Senate (S. 3905) and in the House (H.R. 14643), on which no hearings were held and no action was taken; H.R. 14938, authorizing the Agency for International Development to assist universities in programs of foreign development, particularly in connection with assistance in research, education, training, advisory and technology to developing nations, on which no action was taken.

Considerable interest was also shown in the 1966 session in provision for federal assistance to the social sciences, and in provision for control of research abroad, particularly in the social sciences.

Independent Offices Appropriation Act, 1967

The average citizen—an undefined, nameless, and hypothetical character with considerable public influence—almost certainly does not correctly estimate the importance of Congress' action on the annual measures appropriating funds for the executive branch departments and agencies. In most sessions of the Congress since the establishment of the National Science Foundation, the act which has provided its funds for the coming year has been much the most important legislation affecting the agency.

The bills providing for appropriations are subjected to a very complicated process, as may be illustrated in listing the various steps through which the appropriation for the Foundation for fiscal year 1967 was taken. (This process is, of course, like that through which the appropriations for all the executive departments and agencies are considered and passed by Congress.) It was a lengthy procedure, starting in the late summer and autumn of 1965 with extended conferences between representatives of the Foundation and the appropriate members of the Bureau of the Budget. The President included the amount he recommended in the budget for fiscal year 1967 (July 1, 1966, through June 30, 1967). The portion containing the Foundation's request was considered in the appropriate subcommittees of the Senate and the House Committees on Appropriations, and then by the full committees. H.R. 14921 was introduced in the House on May 5, 1966, "making appropriations for sundry independent executive bureaus, boards, commissions, corporations, agencies, offices, and the Department of Housing and Urban Development for the fiscal year ending June 30, 1967, and for other purposes." Titles I and II were applicable to the National Science Foundation. The bill was reported to the House, accompanied by House Report 1477.

The bill was debated, amended, and passed by the House and by the Senate. Since the two bodies did not agree on all provisions, a conference committee reconciled the two versions. Both houses adopted the conference committee report, and the President signed the bill on September 6, 1966, making it Public Law 89-555. At these various stages, the following amounts were approved for the Foundation: budget request by the President, $525,000,000; recommended by the House in House Report 1859, and passed by the House, $479,999,000; recommended by the Senate in Senate Report 1433 and passed by the Senate, $499,699,000; recommended by the Committee on Conference in House Report 1859, $479,999,000; passed by the House and Senate, and incorporated in Public Law 89-555, $479,999,000.

In reporting the bill, the House Committee recommended the full amount requested by the President with the exception of a cut of the entire amount of $19.7 million requested for Project Mohole (described in Chapter V). It is Congress' relationship to that project to which, in the present connection, principal interest attaches. It is true that Congress had known about it ever since its inception. Hearings on the Foundation's annual appropriations had contained pages and pages of discussion and description. Newspapers and periodicals, both popular and scientific, had published many good articles. Everybody, it was thought, knew about Project Mohole—its scientific merit, the probable spin-off, its international prestige, its tortuous progress, and so on. The question then becomes—what obligation had Congress incurred by continuing to support the project? Even if one admitted that this venture should not have been undertaken in the first place, that inexcusable errors had been committed as it had developed, that it was costing too much—admitting *all* the objections, for purposes of argument—was there by 1966 such a stake in the enterprise that it would have been worse to terminate it than to continue it? Congress, the final authority, concluded that it should end, and so it has, at least for the time being.

Certain important implications can be drawn from Congress' action on the Foundation's appropriation bill in the 1966 session. In the first place, Congress does not generally exercise its constitutional privilege to act on the fine details of appropriations for scientific programs, as it did concerning Project Mohole. Usually they have trusted the Foundation's judgment about the disposition of its funds, and the Mohole episode appears to be a departure from this practice, possibly with serious implications.

In the second place, Congress' action in 1966 did not follow the rather general agreement, reached in 1964, that an annual increase of 15 per cent was necessary to prevent a decline in basic research. This policy lasted only one year. Congress cut the Foundation's requests for funds for fiscal years 1966 and 1967.

The Marine Resources and Development Act

The Marine Resources and Development Act of 1966 (Public Law 89-454) provided for temporary solutions to the problems concerning Congress. Two agencies were established. In the Executive Office of the President, there was the National Council on Marine Resources and Engineering, under the chairmanship of the Vice President, with membership consisting of the secretaries of State, Navy, Interior, Commerce, Health, Education, and Welfare, and Treasury; the chairman of the Atomic Energy Commission; the director of the National Science Foundation; and such others as the President might care to appoint. This Council was to advise the President on the planning and coordination of the over-all national program (It also has other functions under the National Sea Grant College and Program Act, described below.) And there was the Commission on Marine Science, Engineering, and Resources, with fifteen members appointed by the President (not more than five were to be from the federal government) and four "advisory members" appointed by the President from among members of the House and the Senate. The Commission was to review national needs in the field of marine science and engineering, recommend a comprehensive national program, and propose whatever government reorganization it deemed necessary.

The National Sea Grant College and Program Act

In the 1966 session of Congress an important addition was made to the Foundation's oceanographic work by enactment of the National Sea Grant College and Program Act of 1966 (Public Law 89-688). During the 1966 session, many members of the House of Representatives introduced bills on this subject, and several members of the Senate were cosponsors of a similar bill in that house. Although considerable interest was shown in such legislation, it was thought that final action would not be taken, in the 1966 session, and that the proposal would have to be re-introduced in the new Congress in 1967. But the House Committee on Merchant Marine and Fisheries reported H.R. 16559 on August 1, 1966, both houses passed it in September, and the President signed it on October 15— an unusually fast course for a piece of major legislation.

The interest in the sea-grant college proposal undoubtedly was increased by its relationship to the Marine Resources and Engineering Development Act of 1966, passed earlier in the session, and, more generally, to the federal government's comprehensive oceanographic program.

A brief statement of the purposes of H.R. 16559, in House Report 1795, described it as providing for

> . . . the establishment of a program of sea-grant colleges and education, training, and research in the fields of marine science, engineering, and related disciplines as a means of achieving the earliest possible institution of significant national activities related to the development of marine resources in and with relation to the total marine environment.

The term "marine environment" is defined in the bill to include the waters, the surface, and subsurface of the oceans and the Great Lakes, and the resources thereof.

The terms "sea-grant college" and "sea-grant program" emphasize the purpose of establishing programs analogous to the land-grant college programs initiated under the Morrill Act of 1862 which have contributed so much to the development of agriculture in the United States during the past century.

Under the bill the National Science Foundation will be the administering agency. In the exercise of its authority the Foundation will (1) initiate and support educational programs at sea-grant colleges and other suitable institutes and laboratories in the various fields relating to the development of marine resources, (2) initiate and support applied research programs in the various fields relating to the development of marine resources, and (3) encourage and develop advisory programs with the object of disseminating useful information to industry, the scientific community, and the general public.

Not surprisingly, members of both houses who come from states or districts bordering on the oceans were particularly active in support of the sea grant colleges and programs. Attention was called in debate to already existing universities or other institutions supporting oceanographic research programs, including the Institute of Marine Sciences of the University of Miami, the Florida Atlantic University, the Marine Physical Laboratory of the Scripps Institution of Oceanography (California), the California Institute of Technology, the Hawaii Institute of Geophysics, the Hawaii Institute of Marine Biology, the New England Aquarium, the Woods Hole Oceanographic Institute (Massachusetts), and the Southeastern Massachusetts Technical Institute. These agencies would presumably be eligible for assistance under the new program. Members also cited prospective developments in the Great Lakes area and in Long Island. Of course, other areas not fronting on the oceans or the Great Lakes are also engaging in oceanic research. In fact, Athelstan F. Spilhaus, then dean of the inland Institute of Technology at the University of Minnesota, is credited with having originated the sea grant college idea, which he presented in a speech in September, 1963, before the American Fisheries Society.

Bill to Amend the National Science
Foundation Act of 1950

Although this bill "to make changes and improvements in the organization and operation of the Foundation and for other purposes" did not become law in the Eighty-ninth Congress, its history forms an important part of the record of the relationship between Congress and the Foundation. And, eventually, parts of it were put into effect. In the last section of this chapter, there is a summary of the act of July 18, 1968 (Public Law 90-407), which contained a revised version of H. R. 14838 of the Eighty-ninth Congress.

Congress created the Foundation, after several years of consideration, in 1950. In the following years, while it was achieving organization and developing its functions, its principal contact with Congress came each year when the appropriation committees in the Senate and the House held hearings on the Foundation's budget.

As described in earlier sections of this chapter, the House Subcommittee on Science, Research, and Development conducted a thorough review of the work of the Foundation, and in 1966 presented a bill based on its recommendations.

The layman may be interested in considering the lengthy process which precedes the appearance of a major bill. Chairman Daddario's remarks when he introduced H.R. 14838 on July 18, 1966 are quoted, in part, because they reviewed that process and the purposes underlying the bill:

> I would like to stress the point that it was congressional concern which prompted the review of the National Science Foundation. . . . This increased congressional concern has resulted in the proposed legislation which I am presenting today—legislation which has gained the support of both the administration and the scientific community.
>
> Our procedures in reviewing the National Science Foundation

began with a careful survey of the Foundation's operations made at our request by the Library of Congress entitled "The National Science Foundation—A General Review of Its First 15 Years" [House Report 1219, 1966].

In June, 1965, the subcommittee began 7 weeks of public hearings focusing on National Science Foundation's 15 years of operation, its contemporary role, and its outlook for the future. The subcommittee heard testimony from 41 witnesses, representing Government agencies including the National Science Foundation, OST, Department of Defense, NASA, and other departments and agencies, educational institutions, and professional and nonprofit associations. To supplement the testimony, the subcommittee also submitted some 560 written questions to which the witnesses responded. The testimony of the 7 weeks of hearings and the supplementary questions and answers are critically evaluated in the subcommittee report, "The National Science Foundation, Its Present and Future." This report outlined the problems uncovered in the hearings and set forth a number of recommendations for legislative change. In January of 1966, the full Committee on Science and Astronautics unanimously voted to accept this report—House Report No. 1236.

Chairman Daddario introduced a bill on March 16, 1966, based on the recommendations in the Committee report, and hearings were held in April. Witnesses were the directors of the National Science Foundation, the International Scientific and Technological Affairs of the Department of State, the Office of Science and Technology, the executive assistant director of the Bureau of the Budget, the chairman of the National Science Board, and the president of the National Academy of Sciences. By and large, all witnesses were in agreement with the general objectives of the bill. Based on this testimony, the Committee prepared a revised bill (H. R. 14838), and reported it favorably on May 10.

Chairman Daddario commented as follows:

Almost without exception witnesses and other participants were strong in their support of the Foundation, its work, and its value as a national asset. None suggested a reduced or altered role for the National Science Foundation, and yet it did come through that changes were in order. The fact that the Foundation has not kept pace with the demands of society nor adequately oriented itself within the shifting machinery of government was made clear to the committee again and again. The committee's cardinal criticism, then, is that the Foundation has operated, and is largely organized to operate, in a manner which was satisfactory a decade ago but which does not appear adequate for either today or tomorrow.

The Foundation's approach and attitude toward its mission, its relationship with the Executive Office and other agencies of Government, and its legislative machinery, all in varying degree, appear to be in need of overhaul. In general, the Foundation has functioned, and still does, in a manner that is largely passive. It has not itself put a sustained effort into developing substance, form, and direction of the programs it supports. Once granted its annual budget, National Science Foundation has to a large extent followed a practice of waiting for talented outsiders to suggest appropriate projects on which to spend it. However, the time is past due for the Foundation to assume a more positive, dynamic stance. There are at least three good reasons which demand this change.

The reasons Chairman Daddario cited were: (1) the problems of living in today's environment are reaching proportions which are truly monumental; (2) the federal government's interest in, and support of, research and development has become so broad and pervasive that development of national policy concerning it has become correspondingly difficult, whereas the Foundation's contribution seems to have weakened, particularly since the establishment of the several agencies in the Office of the President; and (3) a final reason for a more dynamic posture of the NSF is that the federal departments and agencies depend increasingly on the Foundation to pursue avenues of basic research they themselves cannot provide or afford—a "balance wheel" function.

Although the Daddario statement was rather lengthy, it indicated congressional concern with the situation, and it is useful to the general reader in its presentation of the actual procedures used by a committee in reviewing the work of an agency of the Executive Branch.

The bill was debated and passed by the House on July 18, 1966, without a record vote, two-thirds of the members voting for it under a suspension of the rules. It was sent to the Senate Committee on Labor and Public Welfare, which had already received an identical bill, S. 3465, introduced by Senator Lister Hill (Alabama). No action was taken by this committee, and the measures died at the end of the Eighty-ninth Congress.

H.R. 14838 was a rather complicated measure, and Mr. Daddario in summarizing it named several major recommendations designed to achieve his four previously stated goals. The essence of the bill was the issue of policy control as it related to the relative roles of the director and the National Science Board. Another item of contention, discussed at length in the hearings, was NSF support of applied research, in addition to its traditional role of supporting basic research. Inclusion of the social sciences in the Foundation's legislative mandate won unanimous approval of witnesses. There were differences of opinion, finally resolved, concerning the provision for international activities, and witnesses differed concerning the method of selection of the chairman of the Board. Other provisions produced differences of opinion—for example, those regarding the additional officials and staff, and the directive to maintain data on total federal funds allotted for research to educational institutions, nonprofit organizations, and private contractors. On many other provisions there was either unanimous approval or no dissent. Although the geographical spread of NSF support is a perennial issue before the Congress, no witness at the hearings mentioned the provision on this subject in the bill.

The International Education Act

This act (Public Law 89-698) was not directly aimed at support of education in the sciences, although such education was included in its general terms. The major purpose was to educate American students in international affairs—not to provide education for foreign students. Because this act did not relate to the National Science Foundation, its provisions are not reviewed at this point. One portion, however, has an indirect effect on the Foundation, which should be noted. An amendment proposed by Senator Walter F. Mondale of Minnesota directed the Secretary of Health, Education, and Welfare to conduct a study of the brain drain among students of developing countries and to report the findings to Congress, thus furnishing a factual basis for possible legislation. Senator Mondale explained that his amendment was entirely distinct from a bill he had introduced the same day, described in the following section.

The Proposed International Brain Drain Act of 1966

Although Senator Mondale was successful in obtaining adoption of his amendment to the International Education Act of 1966, he was not so fortunate with another proposal relating to the brain drain, which he introduced with three other senators as cosponsors (S. 3905). In the House, an identical bill (H.R. 14643) was introduced by Representative Donald M. Fraser of Minnesota. In neither body was consideration given to the measure. Possibly, the fact that a study on the extent and nature of the brain drain was to be prepared led members to delay enactment of specific legislation intended to curb it.

Senator Mondale's concern was not so much for the problems of Great Britain and Western European countries, which are not produced primarily by American assistance to scholars and students who come to this country, but rather for the problems of those developing countries whose students come here to study on the assumption that our support of their education is furnished primarily as a form of aid to their countries, rather than as aid to individuals. He emphasized that this purpose fails if they remain in the United States, and consequently, the many different government departments and agencies, the private foundations, and the universities—as the granting agencies—have a responsibility to try to carry out the real purposes for which their programs were established. The bill affected three areas where the United States can have substantial impact—our education of foreign students, our development assistance, and our immigration laws.

Other Bills and the Record

The remaining measures relating to the Foundation introduced in the 1966 session of Congress may be described briefly. All were important and, even though they failed of passage in that session, the subjects with which they dealt remained alive and, in some cases, legislation dealing with them has probably been merely delayed for only a few years.

The 1966 session's legislative record illustrates some of the usual characteristics of this process. The important legislation was, of course, the appropriation act for fiscal year 1967. There were significant policy matters contained in the measure presented by the House Committee on Science and Astronautics, affecting the organization and functions of the Foundation. Considering its complexity and fundamental nature, it can be argued that Congress acted wisely in delaying acceptance. (After further consideration, it was adopted in 1968 with considerable amendment.) Extended consideration by different committees resulted in introduction of several measures that were discussed and debated, but not accepted. This sort of preliminary consideration may, in some cases, be a wasteful procedure, but considering the subjects upon which Congress did not feel ready to take final action it appears that further consideration was indicated. For example, establishment of a Social Science Foundation, or imposing the requirement of annual authorization for the National Science Foundation's appropriation, are proposals for fundamental changes with many direct and side effects. Only extended consideration can make these apparent, and give Congress opportunity to understand very clearly what it is enacting.

CHANGES IN NSF LEGISLATION IN 1968

The preceding section of this chapter described the action in the 89th Congress on a comprehensive measure making changes and improvements in the organization and operation of the National Science Foundation (H.R. 14838). In 1967, a similar bill (H.R. 5404) was introduced, and the House passed it. In May, 1968, the Senate Committee on Labor and Public Welfare reported an amended version, based on hearings and the recommendation of its Special Subcommittee on Science, with Senator Edward M. Kennedy of Massachusetts as its chairman. Both houses of Congress passed the amended version, and the President signed it on July 18, 1968, as Public Law 90-407.

The Foundation's authority was significantly broadened, and the position of the National Science Board as a policy-making body was strengthened. Several important new functions were assigned to the Foundation.

Support for applied research at academic and nonprofit institutions is authorized, at the discretion of the Foundation. The Act also authorizes the support of applied research through profit-making organizations when directed by the President in connection with national problems involving the public interest.

The Foundation is specifically directed to give support to the social sciences. The authority for such support already existed by virtue of general language, but the new Act expressly states the will of Congress that Foundation support in this field should match its support of other sciences.

A new section is added providing that NSF foster and support the development and use of computer and other scientific methods and technologies, primarily for research and education in the sciences.

The NSF is authorized to undertake on its own initiative, or at the request of the Secretary of State or Secretary of Defense, the support of scientific activities relating to international cooperation. This authority joins that previously provided for work to be supported when requested by the Secretary of Defense, but the new authority is discretionary rather than mandatory. Any such activities done at the request of either Secretary must be financed by funds transferred by the requesting Secretary, must be unclassified, and must be identified as being supported as a result of such a request.

The NSF has been required to collect and collate data on national scientific and technical resources. The act provides that the Foundation is to analyze and interpret the data as well. By scientific "resources" are meant scientific and technological manpower and training, facilities, and information.

The NSF is given a new task of ascertaining how much federal money is received each year by each educational institution and appropriate nonprofit organization in the United States.

The act removes the specific statutory basis for the Foundation's activities in the area of weather modification. However, with its new authority to support applied research, the NSF retains authority to continue its broad research support in the area of weather modification. Therefore, the major deletions of substance relate to authority to require reporting to the NSF of private weather modification activities and the NSF power to compel testimony on such activities.

The act also clarifies and broadens a number of the National Science Board's responsibilities and duties, and specifically provides that the Board and the NSF director "shall recommend and encourage the pursuit of national policies for the promotion of basic research and education in the sciences."

One of the Board's major new responsibilities is to render an annual report to the Congress, through the President, on the status and health of American science and its various disciplines. This requirement should not be confused with the annual reports that the Foundation makes on its activities, which will be continued.

Finally, the act makes a number of important changes in the responsibilities of the director, and elevates his position from level III to level II of the federal executive salary schedule. This puts him at the same level as the chairman of the Atomic Energy Commission, the administrators of Veterans Affairs and the National Aeronautics and Space Administration, the secretaries of the Air Force, Army, Navy, and others.

The act provides for appointment of an NSF deputy director by the President by and with the advice and consent of the Senate and elevates the office from level V to level III of the executive salary schedule, and also provides for four assistant directors. These officers, at level V, will be appointed by the President and subject to Senate confirmation.

XIII

The Foundation and
Its Special Publics

The nongovernment institutions with which the Foundation has important connections include the National Academy of Sciences–National Research Council, private foundations, academies, and other nonprofit groups, professional societies, industry, educational institutions, and individual citizens. To an observer completely outside the Foundation, Congress, the executive departments and agencies, and these numerous non-government institutions, it appears rather surprising that the Foundation has been able to establish and maintain good working relations with them and to continue that cooperation with so much respect and good will on the part of all involved. The Foundation is relatively very new, very small, and very weak. The old, large, and strong institutions with which it must work could easily dominate—possibly even destroy —it. But after several years of existence in this hazardous situation, the Foundation has steadily gained in prestige and influence, and it has powerful friends in the government and the universities, the science community, and the general public. After the thorough examination the House Subcommittee on Science, Research, and Development conducted in 1965–66, the Foundation emerged in excellent shape, and the legislation proposed by the subcommittee contained no drastic changes. If it could be determined how the Foundation has accomplished this miracle, the facts would be valuable. The present chapter contains a brief account of the *apparent* facts in the

229

relationships between the Foundation and nongovernment institutions, but the actual working procedures cannot be uncovered—and it is in this area that the Foundation and other agencies have made their relationships effective.

NSF RELATIONSHIPS WITH THE NATIONAL ACADEMY OF SCIENCES–NATIONAL RESEARCH COUNCIL

The National Academy of Sciences is a difficult agency to describe and to understand. One attempt by D. S. Greenberg resulted in a three-part article, which appeared in *Science* in the issues of April 14, 21, and 28, 1967—an interesting and useful report containing much information concerning the policies and practices of the Academy of a kind not to be found in formal, official documents.

In 1863, President Lincoln signed an act of Congress containing a charter for the Academy, a private organization consisting of distinguished scientists who achieve membership through election by the Academy in recognition of their research accomplishments. Of more than 100,000 persons with Ph.D.'s in science, and 2 million others with some professional level of training, the Academy every year selects 45 new members. The total membership is about 740, with 78 foreign associates, and 10 members emeritus.

The charter of the Academy gives it the general duties appropriate to academies of science, and it is also required to act as adviser to the federal government on science matters, but it renders this service only at the request of a government agency, and this agency furnishes necessary funds. The Academy receives no *appropriation* of federal funds. Ten dollar annual dues from its members produces a small operating fund, and its main financial source is gifts from private foundations (for example, the Carnegie Corporation), and contributions, grants, and contract funds from the federal and state agencies, private industries and foundations, scientific societies, and individuals for support of its activities. In 1966, its income from endowment was $398,000, and it received $19.4 million in grants and contracts from other agencies. It pays its way mostly from the overhead fees charged on such projects.

Closely associated with the Academy is the National Research Council, established by the Academy in 1916, at the request of President Wilson. Its purpose is to enable scientists generally to associate their efforts with those of the limited membership of the Academy. The President of the Academy appoints to the Council representatives of scientific and technical societies, designated members of scientific agencies within the federal government, and members-at-large to the different divisions of the Research Council. Although the combined membership of the Academy and the Council is only about 1,000 persons, several thousand scientists and engineers participate in the organizations' activities. Greenberg wrote that the Academy—"an incredibly vast network of activity"—has, in its Washington headquarters, some 700 full-time employees and 4,000 unpaid consultants.

The projects of the Academy and the Council vary widely in the nature, duration, and type of effort required, and a flexible plan of organization is necessary. In general, the organization consists of permanent boards and institutes, committees, subcommittees, and panels, as well as temporary groups for special projects. Their activities include committee deliberations, conferences and symposia, surveys, collection and collation of scientific and technical data, sponsorship of scientific publications and research organizations, administration of public and private funds for research projects and fellowships, and direct publication of technical reports and periodicals.

Only the Foundation and the Academy themselves could give a complete account of their different means of cooperation and its extent, because in large part it is not a matter of formal record. One of the most important methods is the personal contact resulting from interlocking memberships. Many of the top leaders occupy positions at the same time in both agencies, and even more have previously been members of one or the other. The result is that these persons know, from their own experiences, the purposes and policies and programs and officials of the Academy and the Foundation, and as a result they constitute a peculiarly effective means of cooperation in the conduct of the affairs of two agencies. A few examples may be cited.

Detlev Bronk, president of Johns Hopkins University, who had been very active in affairs of the Academy, was its president from 1950 to 1962. This was a period of rapid expansion of federal support for science, and Bronk in his own person served as a link between the Academy and the new science agencies, including the National Science Foundation, which was established in 1950. In 1956 Bronk became president of the National Science Board in the National Science Foundation, and a short time later he was appointed to the President's Science Advisory Committee.

Another example of dual membership is furnished by the position of Philip Handler, who held both the chairmanship of the National Science Board in the NSF, and the chairmanship of an important new committee of the Academy, the Committee on Research in the Life Sciences.

In 1952, the Academy established the U.S. National Committee for the International Geophysical Year (IGY) to represent the United States in the International Council of Scientific Unions and to coordinate the U.S. effort. The Foundation made an initial grant of $5,000 in 1953, and later in the same year a second grant of $22,000. In December, 1953, the National Academy formally requested that the Foundation accept responsibility for obtaining and administering federal funds for participation in the project. At the Foundation's request, Congress appropriated a total of $43.5 million, during fiscal years 1955–59. Other federal agencies received about $100 million of additional funds to participate in the IGY, to provide logistic support, and to launch the Vanguard satellite. The annual reports of the National Academy of Sciences–National Research Council and of the National Science Foundation during the 1953–59 period contained the details of the conduct of the IGY, including the cooperation between the two agencies.

A more tangible type of cooperation is used every year when the Foundation requests the Academy, or the Research Council, to perform studies which the Foundation supports. In fiscal year 1966, the following such grants were made:

Biological and Medical Sciences
  Environmental biology—2 grants, $10,000 and $215,-000.
Mathematical and Physical Sciences
  Astronomy—2 grants, $28,200 and $29,400.
  Chemistry—1 grant, $6,000.
  Physics—2 grants, $18,000 and $11,100.
Engineering Research
  Engineering mechanics—1 grant, $35,000.
  Special projects—2 grants, $15,000 and $15,000.
Environmental Science Research
  Atmospheric sciences—2 grants, $74,400 and $33,700.
Earth Sciences
  2 grants, $118,200 and $1,800.
International Science Research
  5 grants—$30,000, $272,375, $108,300, $75,000, $4,000.
National Research Programs
  U.S. Antarctic research program—1 grant, $43,000.
Science Information Service
  4 grants—$55,800, $1,500, $345,000, $39,900.
Science Education Programs
  Course content improvement—1 grant, $595,850.
Studies of National Resources for Science and Technology
  6 grants—$74,000, $50,000, $75,000, $12,800, $44,-000, $78,000.
Support of the International Biological Program—$315,000.
Geophysics Research Board—$118,200.
Commission on Educational Policy in Agriculture—$113,500.
Support of a Committee on Scientific and Technical Communication—$345,000.

International Science Research, 2 grants:
1. Program of exchange of scientists between National Academy of Sciences, U.S., and to Academy of Sciences, U.S.S.R.—$272,375.
2. International organizations and programs project—$108,305.

In many cases, other public and private agencies work with the National Science Foundation and the National Academy. One such project, dealing with the life sciences, was assigned by the Academy's Committee on Science and Public Policy to a new "Committee on Research in the Life Sciences," in 1966. Its chairman was Philip Handler who was, at the same time, chairman of the National Science Board in the NSF. The study would, it was estimated, take nearly two years to complete, and $500,000 was obligated to it. These funds came from the National Science Foundation, ($75,000), the National Institutes of Health ($300,000), the Smithsonian Institution ($95,000), and the Department of Agriculture ($30,000). Reportedly, the staff director also had tried to get help from the Federation of American Societies for Experimental Biology, the American Institute of Biological Sciences, and other professional societies in the task of gathering and handling the information to be obtained through some 22,000 questionnaires sent to biologists in universities, hospitals, government, and industry. The committee established twenty-three panels of 160 life scientists to review the highlights of the past several years, to define major accomplishments and how they relate to other aspects of the life sciences and other sciences, and to make projections for the future.

This new project of research in the life sciences follows a previously established pattern. The Committee on Science and Public Policy (COSPUP) of the National Academy has conducted five such studies, all financed in whole or in part by the Foundation. The special panels that prepared these reports were all chaired by a representative of the National Science Foundation. COSPUP has initiated or is engaged in studies in other fields of science, which will eventually provide full coverage of all fields; its published reports so far deal with chemistry, physics, plant science, ground-based astronomy, and computer needs in universities.

Although much can be said in support of the present system of simultaneous membership on governmental and nongovernment science agencies, the charge is also made that there are possible adverse results. The Subcommittee on Science, Research, and Development of the House Committee on Science and Astronautics, raised the question of "undue concentration of scientific advice" and, without making a specific recommendation on the subject, submitted it for further inquiry and discussion. The particular example which concerned the subcommittee members arose from the simultaneous membership of individuals on the National Science Board in the Foundation and on other advisory bodies. They could not suggest any immediate, easy solution because, even though some advantages undoubtedly are produced, the disadvantages can not be overlooked. The "inbreeding" of science advisers tends to produce a combining of the functions of prosecutor, judge, and jury in the hands of a few highly placed scientists and engineers. It is doubtful, furthermore, that these persons have sufficient time to do a satisfactory job in each of several capacities. But if there were to be a prohibition of such overlapping memberships, some good people might refuse to serve on the National Science Board simply because they would not wish to be automatically excluded from other federal science activities during their six-year term on the Board. Balanced against these disadvantages, is the obvious advantage of having at least some members who can act as liaison, and who are familiar with the over-all picture of federal science activities.

THE NSF AND NONGOVERNMENT NONPROFIT GROUPS

When the National Science Foundation was established, it was modeled in many ways on the private foundations. The most important difference between them was believed to be the source of their funds—the NSF would receive federal appropriations and the private foundations would continue to expend their endowments, often from wealthy individuals (the Rockefeller, Carnegie, Sloan, Ford, and Russell Sage foundations, for example). But as time has gone on it has become evident that this difference in source of funds has produced many other unexpected differences, of basic importance.

Attention is called to two recent statements by a distinguished representative of the private foundations, Warren Weaver, who for many years guided the Rockefeller Foundation in its support of basic sciences. In *Scientific Research* (July, 1967), Weaver expressed the view that, although the foundations contributed only about 1 per cent of the amount of the government's budget for basic research, their contributions have a significance and importance completely out of proportion to their relative magnitude. The differences, as he described them, indicate that government grants and private foundation grants supplement, rather than duplicate, each other. Some quotations from his statement indicate his judgment as to these differences:

> Anyone who has had any experience in Washington knows that there are necessary and proper limitations to Government support. Thus, the Government has to be concerned under our democratic procedures with supporting what you might call the national average and be concerned in trying to raise the national average.
>
> Private foundations, however, can go back to the elements of democracy which Thomas Jefferson emphasized so strongly and be concerned with what you could call the aristocracy of excellence. It is difficult for the Government to be concerned with the aristocracy of excellence, but I think it is absolutely essential that within the democratic procedure you have some mechanism that does treat the aristocracy of excellence—that recognizes it and supports it.
>
> Therefore, you will find that foundations on the whole, particularly the big foundations, are concerned to set standards, to establish what have sometimes been called peaks of excellence. Then it is the Government's job to try to bring the great mass

closer and closer up to those standards. This is a double-jointed attack on the problem that I think our society cannot do without.

In their search for excellence the private foundations can also be more venturesome than the government. Among sources of Government funds there is a certain inevitable tendency towards conformity. The moment you try to become venturesome in Government you're sticking your neck out in the direction of the other end of Pennsylvania Avenue and that's a very dangerous direction in which to stick your neck out if you're getting your money from the Government.

Finally, Government agencies are necessarily and properly slower to move. I think they *should* be slow to move, but I think it's very important for society to have some other agencies around which it can move more rapidly. It is true that on large proposals, foundations sometimes take a considerable time to make a thorough study, but it is also true that almost all foundations can move more quickly when circumstances quite clearly justify it and do move more quickly particularly on critically needed smaller amounts.

In a letter to *Science,* December 1, 1967, Weaver made the following comparison of the Foundation's and the federal government's support of research:

Federal sources of support are renewed biannually; private foundations characteristically have fixed capital sums, and their continuing capacity to make grants rests upon the uncommitted portion of their income. If private foundations accept continuing responsibility for support, they are thereby adopting a policy of gradual suicide. Federal sources, in contrast, are able to have, and do and should have a responsibility for the general health of our educational institutions, this involving a broad national obligation to furnish the continuing support which cannot be obtained from local sources.

The conclusion to be drawn from Weaver's analysis is that the National Science Foundation and the private foundations have a complementary relationship, rather than a cooperative one. In the case of other nongovernmental agencies, the Foundation makes grants to them or contracts with them, expending federal funds, but this does not happen with the nonprofit foundations. The private philanthropic foundations and the National Science Foundation exchange policy and program information as their principal means of contact.

The National Science Foundation has shown its interest in the nonacademic, nonprofit institutions, including research institutes, professional societies, and philanthropic foundations, by including data concerning their activities in its surveys and analyses of the national science research and education effort.

Some examples of contracts with private nonprofit institutions in the Foundation's 1966 listing of grants and contracts were:

Center for Advanced Study in the Behavioral Sciences (Stanford, Calif.)
   Grant for advanced study and research in social science —$53,800.

Bernice P. Bishop Museum (Honolulu, Hawaii)
   Grant for ecological survey of land anthropods, Anvers Island, Antarctica—$35,500.

Battelle Memorial Institute (Columbus, Ohio)
   Contract for science information exchange requirements study—$26,800.
   Contract for survey of science information manpower in engineering and the natural sciences—$14,725.

Graduate Research Center of the Southwest (Dallas, Texas)
   Grant for a cooperative program in seismology between the Earthquake Research Institute of Tokyo University and the Graduate Center—$9,700.

The Foundation's program of financing visiting scientists in secondary schools, in 1966, was carried out in thirty-five states by their respective academies of science, each of which received a grant for the purpose. In the other states, different professional societies conducted these programs with grants from the Foundation.

THE NSF AND THE PROFESSIONAL SOCIETIES

The direct relationship between the Foundation and the professional societies of scientists (in addition to the National Academy of Sciences itself, the most prestigious of all the professional groups) is produced through grants and contracts. An important example is furnished in the operation by the Foundation of the National Register of Scientific and Technical Personnel. In 1966, twelve professional scientific societies were distributing questionnaires to their members, seeking data for inclusion in the Foundation's biennial publication of the Register.

In the listing of NSF grants and contracts for fiscal year 1966, the following examples of contracts for this purpose were listed:

American Anthropological Association	$ 6,750
American Chemical Society	97,170
American Psychological Association	24,000
Center for Applied Linguistics	26,858
American Economic Association	22,814
Federation of American Societies for Experimental Biology	873
American Meteorological Society	27,400
American Institute of Physics	60,550
Modern Language Association of America	1,465
American Mathematical Society	44,526

In the same year, the Foundation listed grants or contracts for studies of national resources for science and technology with the American Association for the Advancement of Science, the American Association of Junior Colleges, the American Council on Education, the National Academy of Sciences—National Research Council, and the National Science Teachers Association.

The American Association for the Advancement of Science (AAAS) plays a significant role in the affairs of the Foundation, as it does in those of other federal science agencies. The AAAS is open to anyone interested in science. It has a large membership drawn from all areas of science, and its annual meetings are events of public interest, covered by the national press. *Science,* the weekly publication of the Association, so often quoted in these pages, has many lead articles about the Foundation and many editorials and news items and comments about it. In 1966, the Association received a grant of $595,850 from NSF in support of the Commission on Science Education.

Other influential organizations are those with memberships drawn from the many scientific disciplines, including those listed above in this section, and many others. Their members serve on the advisory committees, councils, and panels of the Foundation and, as individual researchers, they receive grants for research.

Although the professional societies directly concerned with science are possibly the most influential of all the different types of societies in their relationships with the Foundation, there are others which should be noted. The Foundation's science education activities constitute a large portion of its work, and university-connected organizations and professional education societies are naturally interested in the Foundation's numerous programs.

For example, the National Association of College and University Officers recently opened its national offices in Washington, after having had only a local representation in the Capitol since 1961. The Association has a membership of about 1,000 institutions. The National Association of State Universities and Land Grant Colleges, the American Council on Education, the Association of Higher Education, the Association of American Universities, the Associated Colleges of the Midwest and many other similar associations keep in very close touch with all government agencies—including, of course, the National Science Foundation—which furnish federal funds for different science education activities.

THE NSF AND INDUSTRY

The relationships between the federal government and industry, and between certain of the science agencies of the federal government and industry, are of very great importance, but, in the nature of the case, the National Science Foundation and industry are relatively little involved with each other. With one exception, the Foundation has had few projects in which as an operating agency it has had to handle the huge contracts for research and development that the Department of Defense, the Atomic Energy Commission, and the National Aeronautics and Space Administration have managed. The exception, of course, was Project Mohole, which is discussed in some detail in other chapters of this book. It was operated by the Foundation through contract with an industrial firm, with less than happy results.

This does not mean that the Foundation and industry have no interest in each other and no contacts. The following examples are to be found in the Foundation's listing of grants and contracts for fiscal year 1966:

Alpine Geophysical Associates, Inc. (Norwood, N.J.)
Two contracts for operation and maintenance of government vessel for research, and administrative support of an oceanographic research program—$144,075 and $1,151,562.

Astrofilms, Inc. (Kensington, Md.)
Creative editing, matching, music and effects, editorial and laboratory preparation of films—$15,000.

Computer Usage Company, Inc. (Washington, D.C.)
Three contracts for analyses, programing, and computer services to process data on three subjects to be used in NSF's published reports—$10,000, $12,551, and $19,673.

American Express Co. (Washington, D.C.)
Transportation services related to non-government travel in the U.S. research program—$75,000.

Goodyear Aerospace Corporation (Akron, Ohio)
Application of associative memory to chemical information storage and retrieval—$75,846.

Educational Services, Inc. (Watertown, Mass.)
General services to centers in Latin America engaged in activities for the improvement of the teaching of physics —$37,700.

Global Marine Exploration Co. (Los Angeles, Calif.)
Development of deep ocean coring tool—$79,785.

Douglas Aircraft Co., Inc. (Santa Monica, Calif.)
Conducting a conjugate point riometer program—$217,-400.

Further evidence of cooperation between the Foundation and industry can be found in the listings of members of the National Science Board and the different advisory committees, councils, and commissions. Among the Board members for fiscal 1966 were the president of Picker X-Ray Corp. (White Plains, N.Y.), and the vice president and chief scientist of the International Business Machines Corp. (Armonk, N.Y.). The advisory committees included members who were officials of such companies as Bell Telephone Laboratories, Westinghouse Electric Corp., Lockheed Aircraft Corp., Smith, Kline, and French Laboratories, Squibb Institute for Medical Research, Travelers Insurance Co., International Business Machines, and the Ford Motor Co.

As part of its science policy planning activities, the Foundation has made several major surveys and analyses of industrial research and development. Arrangements have been made for improving exchange of policy and program information with large industrial research-oriented industrial corporations, the National Industrial Conference Board, and the Industrial Research Institute.

THE NSF AND EDUCATIONAL INSTITUTIONS

In order to avoid repetition, only general reference is made at this point to the complex of relationships with schools, colleges, and universities, which are the most important of the Foundation's contacts other than those with Congress and the departments and agencies of the executive branch. Other parts of this book have dealt with different aspects of the Foundation's relationships with educational institutions, but since it has been estimated that some $450 million of the approximately $500 million of NSF annual funds go, directly or indirectly, into these institutions, the importance of these interrelationships can scarcely be overemphasized.

The Foundation's announced goals in this area center around clearly identified needs, which have been defined as intended to:

Further the scientific training of high-quality graduate students and scientists.

Improve the subject-matter competence of teachers of science, mathematics, or engineering at all academic levels.

Provide modern materials of instruction and courses of study.

Increase the scientific knowledge and experience of talented high school students and undergraduate college students.

Improve science instruction at the undergraduate level by assisting institutions in acquiring modern instructional scientific equipment.

Improve the American public's understanding of science.

THE NSF AND THE GENERAL PUBLIC

An editorial entitled "Incomprehensible Science" in *The New York Times* on November 6, 1966, stated the problem of public understanding of science very clearly:

The problem of communication between the scientific community and the rest of the world is again raised sharply by the 1966 Nobel Prizes in physics and chemistry. The work of the winners, Profs. Alfred Kastler and Robert S. Mulliken, has certainly been distinguished, but equally certainly it has hitherto been almost unknown to the general public. Even now it is unlikely that either man's writings will appear on best-seller lists. Their contributions to man's knowledge of atomic and molecular theory are intrinsically highly technical and complicated.

This communications problem tends to get worse as the volume of scientific data grows rapidly and as scientists penetrate ever deeper into regions removed from ordinary experience. The extreme has already been achieved in pure mathematics where there is now almost no popular understanding of what is going on at the frontiers of mathematical research. It would be helpful if there were a Nobel Prize in mathematics to call attention annually to the outstanding work being done in that field.

Yet the need has probably never been greater than now for adequate public understanding of what scientists are up to. One reason is the tremendous impact of science and technology upon modern civilization. A second reason is the heavy dependence scientific research now must place upon financial support from Government agencies, which in turn must look to the layman and to Congress for their budgets. The poorer the communication between scientists and non-scientists the greater the danger that wrong decisions may be made in a period when the competition among scientists and scientific fields for limited research funds is becoming unprecedentedly intense.

The need for public understanding of science and—in the present connection—of the government's science policies and programs has been stressed repeatedly, particularly since these programs began to grow so rapidly, some ten years ago. In 1959, the President's Science Advisory Committee in its report "Education for the Age of Science," stated that science, engineering, and technology had been responsible for a host of changes, that such changes would continue to occur, and that the people of the United States must accept and support them.

The report reviewed briefly the accelerated rate of growth in all fields of science and the resultant effects upon the life of every contemporary man, every day, and stated:

> If an individual is ignorant of science he must guess what to do or else believe what he is told. Even if he is told what to do by an expert, he has no way to check on this advice or even to understand it. . . .
>
> To be able to think beyond the press releases and publicity statements, to understand the background of national debate

requires a greater comprehension of space problems than that provided by science fiction or the comic strip.

Yet the field of space research is only one important field of modern technology, which is of concern to the average citizen. There are other fields involving communication, transportation, and human health. But are there still others which we do not recognize at all? Is it because no comparable Sputnik has awakened us? The shocks provided by achievement elsewhere may not be an adequate guide to our progress or our efforts. A national effort is required to strengthen our scientific and technological efforts in all fields, aimed at the advance of knowledge and the enhancement of the general welfare.

In the Committee's judgment, past curricula have not adequately prepared college graduates to understand, or even to be interested in, science, and they have not made efforts after graduation to remedy this lack. The report continued:

A democratic citizenry today must understand science in order to have a wide and intelligent democratic participation in many national decisions. Such decisions are being made now. They cannot be postponed for twenty years while we are improving our present educational system so that its products will constitute a significant fraction of the mature voting population. There is, therefore, no escape from the urgency of providing high-grade and plentiful adult education in science now, planned for those who are unperpared even in the fundamentals.

Whatever medium is used, science must, first of all, be made as interesting to the bystander as it is exciting and inspiring to the scientist. Citizens will not submit themselves to adult education in science simply as a response to bugle calls to duty. The excitement and interest of science must somehow be transmitted.

In the years since the PSAC report was published, views similar to those quoted have appeared in increasing numbers, and more recent statements express even greater urgency than did the early ones, and some outstanding programs have been established. In Seattle, the Pacific Science Center furnishes an example of a successful achievement in the popularization of science. The St. Louis Committee for Environmental Information publishes an attractive magazine, *Scientist and Citizen,* and carries on many scientific information activities in that city.

The professional organizations are making strong efforts to establish better relationships with the public. The National Academy of Science has an active committee on Science and Public Policy; the Academy of Engineering has a committee on Engineering and Public Policy; the American Chemical Society has a committee on Chemistry and Public Affairs; the Federation of American Societies for Experimental Biology has an office of Public Affairs and a committee on Engineering and Public Policy. The Scientists' Institute for Public Information, founded in 1963 by scientists from some two dozen information committees, has as its chief purpose providing the public with objective, understandable scientific data bearing on public policy issues. All agree that the public cannot make correct decisions on such issues without adequate information, which the scientists must furnish if they expect to have the support of the public in their requests for ever-increasing amounts of government support.

Where does the National Science Foundation fit into this situation? Activities aimed at better public understanding of science have always been a part of the Foundation's program, although from a budget standpoint this activity occupies a minor place. In terms of dollars, the public understanding program, which was begun in 1960 with a little more than $300 thousand, has continued at a level not exceeding $500 thousand. The House Committee on Science and Astronautics in House Report 1236 (1966) stated its belief that the scale of this program deserved future attention to see whether it is too small and suggested that a level of about 1 per cent of the science education program would not seem excessive.

Usually, the Foundation has not included a separate listing of its projects in this area in its annual report of grants and contracts, but in 1963 twelve such projects were listed, totaling about $391,000. The largest grant, $100,000, was made to the Pacific Science Center Foundation in Seattle, for support of the Center. Several symposiums and seminars were financed—for science writers in rapidly advancing areas of physics, on the public understanding of the role of science in society, on news writing for rural community press, on present frontiers in physics, on health sciences reporting, and on the living state. Other projects which received grants were for studies of the relationships among the natural sciences, a new public information service to promote scientific understanding and a comprehensive program for development of public understanding in science, the filming of a new educational television series, and preparation of a radio astronomy exhibit.

The Foundation's activities aimed at increasing public understanding of science are conducted under its program for advanced science education activities in the Division of Graduate Education in Science. The Foundation's other activities in collecting, publishing, and disseminating scientific information are designed for the specific use of scientists and, in general, are too technical for nonscientists.

XIV

The National Science Foundation, Present and Future

Perhaps it is not really necessary to conclude this book with a chapter in which the record of the Foundation is evaluated and its future career predicted, because almost every chapter has touched upon these two subjects. However, as a more general evaluation, this final chapter contains examples of assessments by the Congress, by the Foundation itself, and by individuals competent to judge the Foundation's record and to consider its future. To begin with the last category, no single statement seems more apt a summary than one made by Lee A. DuBridge.

Dr. DuBridge, president of the California Institute of Politics since 1946, has a long record in which he has combined the careers of a physicist and university teacher, a university administrator, government official, and eminent member of the science community. He was a member of the Atomic Energy Commission from 1946 to 1952, and a member of the National Science Board in NSF, 1950–54 and 1958–64, and is a member of the National Academy of Sciences. Through this long and distinguished career he has achieved a position of unquestioned authority on the science policy, functions, and organizations of the federal government. He was named by President Nixon to succeed Dr. Hornig as Presidential science adviser.

An article of his in *Science* (August 11, 1967), discussed university basic research, but dealt to a considerable extent with the broader problems of the government's role in support of basic research—one of the National Science Foundation's major functions.

Dr. DuBridge wrote that the nation's program of basic research in science is at a critical juncture, and that its future depends on the outcome of debates in scientific circles, the public press, Congress, and offices of the executive branch. The scientific community is, of course, deeply involved in this debate, but the decisions, which are matters of public policy, will not be made by the scientists. The case for basic research in modern science must, he wrote, emerge from the scientists themselves:

> The case for these values of science can be, and has been, documented time and time again. If people are tired of hearing of the great results of the researches of Galileo, Newton, Faraday, Maxwell, Einstein, and the rest, there are many other examples that can be set forth. I suggest that we set them forth, repeatedly and convincingly. This is the case that must be documented. Man *is* better off today than he was 300 years ago, and science has done much to this end by combating superstition and prejudice, by allaying hunger and disease, by laying the base for technological advance. If the world's troubles still seem tragic and complex, this is so not because we have too much knowledge but because we have not learned how to use all our knowledge effectively.

But, Dr. DuBridge asked:

> . . . is a major overhaul of [our] system [of supporting science research] either necessary or desirable? I know of no widely accepted proposals for such an overhaul. Most of the arguments and misunderstandings about the total effectiveness of the system are based on conflicting opinions as to the relative importance of the various objectives of the mission-oriented agencies. It is said by some that we are spending too much on space and not enough on cancer—or vice versa; too much on military development and not enough on weather modification or oceanography or atomic energy—or, again, vice versa.

Now these national-policy objectives are determined by the

legislative and executive branches of the government on the basis of considerations having little to do with the progress of basic science.

If the government wishes (as I believe it should) to develop a more adequate and more balanced program for strengthening American science per se, then it should charge suitable agencies (principally the National Science Foundation) with this particular task, and provide funds adequate for carrying it out.

As I have said, there is nothing basically wrong with the system. But there *are* serious dangers ahead in its current operations. The degree to which mission-oriented agencies of government will invest their precious funds in the rather long-range benefits to be expected from basic science will vary. Already there are pressures for concentrating on more immediate results. . . . Mission-oriented agencies are, understandably, in a hurry. Can we afford to let the basic knowledge so necessary for future progress depend on the winds of political and economic pressures which blow hot or cold today?

A ready solution is at hand. The National Science Foundation *can* be depended on to look to the long-range future. It can be depended upon to recognize the cultural as well as the practical values of basic science. It can serve as the balance wheel to promote the broad advance of science—if its research budget is substantially increased.

The budget levels for NSF are determined by the Bureau of the Budget and by the House and Senate appropriation committees, agencies to which scientists at large and the general public have almost no access. The burden of presenting the needs of science thus falls almost solely on the members of the Board and the staff of NSF, aided only by the behind-the-scenes work of the President's Science Advisory Committee.

Here is a serious flaw in an otherwise viable system. Herein lies the need for a widespread public discussion of the issues— so that *all* congressmen and senators become aware of the real values and needs of basic science, and of the critical role which can and should be played by NSF. Presumably, only wide public support will have the required influence on the appropriate committees and offices.*

* Copyright 1967 by the American Association for the Advancement of Science.

Congressional Assessment of the NSF

Before 1965, the principal means through which Congress evaluated the work of the Foundation was the process by which it appropriated funds each year to cover the activities of the following year. Congress' conclusions were summed up each year, after more or less debate on the floor of the two houses, in the amounts of appropriations finally granted. The rapid increase in these amounts during the period indicates general congressional approval of the Foundation and its activities, although it must be noted that the Foundation always asked for more than Congress was willing to grant. As discussed in detail earlier, Congress since 1950 has amended the National Science Foundation Act a number of times, indicating that the original provisions were not entirely satisfactory in operation, in some cases chiefly because of changes in the over-all federal-science relationship, and in other cases because of the rapid increase in the whole public and private science activity. Before 1965 few of the legislative enactments made fundamental changes in the basic law governing the Foundation.

In the course of the action, starting in 1965, that culminated in a new law in 1968, there was a thorough discussion of all aspects of the organization and functions of the NSF. Representative Daddario, chairman of the subcommittee preparing the new bill, stated in the opening paragraph of House Report 1219 (1965) that the inquiry was motivated, not by a presumption of agency mismanagement, but by a recognition of the development of new problems, and also because there was "recognition that a current of scientific opinion visualizes the Foundation as occupying an even more significant role in the future if it is to carry out its legislative mandate to promote the progress of science."

He described the complex situation within which the Foundation operates, illustrating the difficulties encountered by the subcommittee in trying to evaluate its record and to make recommendations for its future role, adding: "The Congress is now faced with unprecedented choices in which the support of research becomes only one of a number of new elements competing for Federal funds—whether for educational needs, anti-poverty measures, support for the arts and humanities, or meeting new problems of urbanization such as environmental pollution."

It is scarcely necessary to state that the conditions encountered in 1965 have, if possible, become even more complex and more urgent as they have developed in the years following. When he introduced the bill (H.R. 14838) in July, 1966, Chairman Daddario stated that his subcommittee's report was, and was intended to be, a critical one. But, he explained:

> The subcommittee does not mean critical in the sense of pointing fingers at failure, mismanagement, or nonfeasance, but critical in the sense of evaluating a major ongoing operation of government against the backdrop of the future and the needs of the Nation.
>
> The subcommittee's inquiry has, inevitably, disclosed some shortcomings of the first type. On balance, however, their effect has been so far submerged by the main positive thrust of the Foundation's usefulness that concentration on them by the subcommittee could not be considered warranted at this point.
>
> Shortcomings of the second type are something else again. Still, these stem less from personal aptitudes, or lack thereof, than from the swift tempo of contemporary living and the unparalleled growth of science and technology. The moment and impact of each is having a highly significant effect upon the other, to the point of much mutual dependence. Put another way, the problems of current government, as well as everyday life, clearly depend upon science and technology for at least a part of their solution—an important part. Correspondingly, science and technology, which today more than ever cannot afford to become stagnant, must rely to a large extent upon government and the motives provided by the pressing difficulties of modern society to induce a satisfactory rate of evolution.
>
> It is within this context of scientific, political, and social interaction that the subcommittee evokes its cardinal criticism; namely, that the Foundation is operating, and is largely organized to operate, in a manner which was satisfactory a decade

ago but which does not appear adequate for either today or tomorrow.

The Foundation's approach and attitude toward its mission, its relationship with the Executive Office and other agencies of Government, and its legislative machinery all—in varying degree—appear to be in need of overhaul.

. . . the fact is that the Foundation has not kept pace with the demands of society nor adequately oriented itself within the shifting machinery of government. . . .

Fundamentally it may be said that the Foundation has functioned, and still does, in a manner that is largely passive. It has not itself put a sustained effort into developing substance, form, and direction of the programs it supports. Once granted its annual budget, NSF has to a large extent followed a practice of waiting for talented outsiders to suggest appropriate projects on which to spend it.

There have been at least three reasons for adhering to this procedure. One is that so far as effectively supporting basic research is concerned, the system has generally worked well; it has been a boon to the scientific community and particularly to the science-minded colleges and universities. Without fluid NSF support, the state of basic research in the Nation—and the quantity and quality of American scientists and engineers—would be far less satisfactory than they are. A second reason is that by waiting for proposals from private sources, the Foundation has been able to tap a vast reservoir of ingenuity, imagination and scientific competence which it could not itself begin to duplicate. A third reason is that the legislative charter of the Foundation does not generally permit in-house research or technological activity.

Nonetheless, the time is past due for the Foundation to assume a more positive, dynamic stance. . . .

There should be, and is, a scientific and technological stature about the Foundation sufficient to warrant an extraordinary voice in the science policy chambers of the administration. NSF is the only Federal agency with an exclusive scientific mandate. It should make itself heard, and should be listened to, accordingly. While the Foundation's mission may be less tangible or focused than those of other government agencies, it is equally as real. If there is a disposition on the part of either the Executive or the Foundation to regard NSF viewpoints as less significant vis-à-vis the so-called "mission oriented" agencies, that disposition should be erased.

It is not clear from the record to date whether the Foundation is yet visualizing and preparing for the dynamic role which circumstances seem to be thrusting upon it. It appears doubtful.

There are, however, a number of changes and/or innovations which the subcommittee believes should take place in order for the Foundation to assume the responsibilities described. In general, they are as follows:

1. The Foundation needs to supplement its traditional philosophy with positive, forward-looking plans and programs. Its position within the executive family should be upgraded and its influence increased.

2. The character and functions of the National Science Board should be strengthened so as to give it a more lubricated and flexible position in governing NSF affairs. At the same time, the Board should also develop a more potent and utilized capability as a national advisory body available to both executive and legislative councils, with particular reference to science resources and policies governing them.

3. The authority of the Foundation's Director should be widened so as to give him power to administer NSF affairs with a minimum of protocol or the necessity of going through pro forma routine. . . .

4. In addition, it is submitted that a number of other contemporary questions and issues involving NSF deserve further scrutiny. These are matters which have been, or are being, discussed around the conference tables of both government and the scientific community. Administrative or legislative action on them may be required in the not-too-distant future.

Chairman Daddario listed the following concerns: (1) the appointment and tenure of the director, (2) the danger of limited viewpoint which may arise from too much inbreeding within the Government's science advisory bodies, (3) the proper balance in the Foundation's support of education and teaching as opposed to its support of research, (4) the proper balance in the Foundation's support of engineering vis-à-vis the physical sciences, and (5) the methods and emphasis of

NSF support of new curricula for the teaching of science and technology.

It is sometimes proposed that the National Science Foundation become a part of a new department of science or that in some form the Foundation and the science agencies of the Office of the President be combined. But, in the great majority of cases, the proposals are for increased funds to enable the Foundation to expand its present programs, for better organization to improve its operations, for addition of new functions, for better techniques of operation, for better relationships with other elements of the science community—in short, for strengthening and improving the Foundation as a valuable part of that community.

The subject was of concern in the hearings before the Subcommittee on Science, Research, and Development of the House Committee on Science and Astronautics. At those hearings, in the summer of 1965, Don K. Price, dean of the Graduate School of Public Administration at Harvard, appeared as a witness. Price has been a participant in the broad area of federal science policy since the early 1940's, and perhaps no one understands the whole history of the Foundation as well as he does. In his prepared statement, he said that it seemed to him that the subcommittee had opened for discussion one of the most significant political problems of our time—the way in which science and government interact. In commenting on the role of the Foundation, he noted the necessity to include consideration of the ways in which the executive branch develops its scientific policies and the relations of the various research programs of the government. He hoped that other witnesses would agree that the Foundation has been "a remarkable success . . . a most successful political invention" and continued:

> But success, in affairs of state, is never a permanent thing: new problems arise for any institution just because it is successful. And the problems that we can see ahead in the Government's support of science and related educational activities warrant a careful and critical review of the principles on which the Foun-

dation was conceived 20 years ago, 5 years before it was actually brought to birth.

. . . The main issues seem to me, as I look back on them, to fall in two categories. One was the problem of the relation of science to political authority; the other was the relation of basic science to applied science.

Of the two, the relation of science to political authority was the more fundamental, at least from the point of view of a political theorist.

Yet in retrospect, this particular problem was solved so easily, and so much to everyone's satisfaction, that today the issue almost seems a phony one. By contrast, the problem of the relation of the Foundation, with its basic research programs, to the Government's program of applied research, and to the potential new programs of research and education, seems a much more difficult one, even though of less theoretical significance.

Price then discussed the general approach that should be taken to the second issue—the relation of basic to applied science, giving an outline of desirable lines of future policy:

First, I see no point in the notion of a single Department of Science. It seems to me as useless to try to segregate science as to allocate responsibility for thinking about policy; both are parts of the job of every agency of Government.

Second, I would not try to prohibit any agency that supports applied research from supporting a small proportion of basic research along with it. The borderline between "basic" and "applied" is impossible to police. But more important, it seems to me highly desirable to have basic research supported by a variety of sources.

Third, I should think the National Science Foundation would do well to concentrate on its original purpose, in the main, of support for basic research and related educational activities. The Foundation is the Nation's main means for insuring that the varied purposes of agencies with particular programs do not pull science away from the lines of development that its own leaders think most fruitful.

David Allison, senior editor of *International Science and*

Technology, discussing these subcommittee hearings, wrote that

> . . . the Congress of today views the Foundation as a permanent part of the governmental establishment. It views the support of science, including science education, as a national commitment. And that is the drastic change. This year, for instance, the Congress will appropriate some $500 million to the Foundation. This is 2000 times the amount it allocated in that first year of NSF's existence, and 130 times the allocation of the second year. In fact, the Congress will allocate more money to NSF during this next year than it allocated *in toto* during the first ten years of the Foundation's life.

However, Allison pointed out, the hearings by the Subcommittee on Science, Research, and Development revealed that Congress was also clearly impatient with the Foundation. Support of science could no longer be justified solely on the grounds that science is "a good thing." Now, the justification carried a demand for responsible guidance, and the basic question before the Subcommittee was whether the Foundation could assume the responsibility of this support.

During debate in the Senate on the appropriation for fiscal year 1968 for the Foundation, Senator Fred Harris of Oklahoma made a strong effort to obtain an increase in the amount recommended by the Senate Committee. In part, his argument was based on the increased cost of basic research and on what he considered to be an "erroneous assumption" that there has been "a proliferation of basic research in pure science now conducted by private industry as well as the Government." In 1963–66, expenditures by private industry had grown at the rate of only 7 per cent, and those by the federal government by only 11 per cent per year. He continued:

> Surely this is not a "proliferation" of support for basic research, when the increased cost of research and increases in the number of new scientists are taken into account. There has been a 6 to 7 per cent increase per year in the cost of research, due to the higher cost of living and greater complexity and sophistication of the scientific research effort. This figure . . . is accounted

for by some simple facts: the rising costs of salaries, need for specialized technical personnel, more complicated equipment, and others.

. . . the . . . increases to which I have alluded, are in reality little more than just holding the line.

THE FOUNDATION SELF-ASSESSED

The federal departments and agencies, including the Foundation, are inevitably compelled to assess their own accomplishments, and, naturally, they tend to take a favorable view of them. But even though these evaluations come from interested parties, they are entitled to serious consideration. No one outside the agencies has the detailed knowledge of operations that their top executives have. The Bureau of the Budget, the appropriations committees of the Senate and the House, and the Senate and House themselves have to be convinced each year that a particular agency—in this case, the Foundation—has been doing a good job, that it must have at least as much money for the next year as it has currently available, and, in almost every case, that it can do even more and do it better if it has more money. Since the Bureau of the Budget and the congressional committees and their subcommittees are very well informed concerning the work of the Foundation, reasonable accuracy and restraint must be exercised in presenting its case. Consequently, what the Foundation has to say about itself is one of the principal sources that must be used in assessing its accomplishments.

As this book has stressed, the record of the Foundation's own evaluation of its work is to be found in its annual reports, the published hearings and reports of the Senate and House committees on appropriations, certain reports of the House Committee on Science and Astronautics, occasional articles by the director or the chairman of the board, and the coverage by *Science* and other professional publications. A few selections from these sources may be cited.

The Foundation, in its first annual report, recognized that it was breaking new ground, and that Congress had created a new type of government agency to insure that Federal funds spent in support of scientific research were wisely used. It stated its belief that, over the years, the new agency would succeed.

Five years later, in the 1956 annual report, the chairman of the National Science Board, Detlev W. Bronk, wrote in glowing terms of the dramatic decade in the development of science in the United States since the end of World War II, saying, in part:

> These remarkable achievements have been enabled in large degree by the greatly increased financial support of scientific research and teaching by our Federal Government and by private industry. The National Science Foundation has done much to foster those developments. The Foundation has even heavier responsibilities and greater opportunities in the years ahead in order that our accelerating scientific progress may be sustained by the discovery of new knowledge and by the enthusiasm of newly trained scientists.
>
> The National Science Foundation is remarkable for the vast number of those who carry out its functions in all parts of our country. A small administrative organization relies upon the freely given advice and expert judgment of thousands of scientists drawn from universities and other research institutions and from industrial and Government laboratories. On their advice funds are granted for the work of scientists and teachers in universities, colleges, and schools in every state of the Nation. The freedom and integrity of our private cultural institutions are thus preserved. The culture of every state in the Union is thus enriched. It is truly a *National* Science Foundation.

In what is often referred to as the "post-Sputnik" era, great concern existed as to the status and the future of science. The Foundation's involvement was described in its annual report for 1959 in the opening section, entitled "Reappraisal and Reorganization—the Status of Science in the United States, 1958–1959," and particularly in one portion entitled "Changing Role of the National Science Foundation in Federal Science Organization," from which the following is quoted:

As the discussions continued throughout Washington and the Nation on the reorganization of science, a look at the National Science Foundation showed that within NSF changes were taking place that affected, and were affected by, the national concern for better science. There was increasing evidence, as outlined above, that other agencies were looking to NSF for leadership in specific situations involved with Federal support of scientific research. Too, NSF is assuming increased leadership toward the objective that Federal support of basic research be reasonably balanced and consistent with the varying needs of the different scientific disciplines.

Historically, the Foundation has depended upon the thinking of scientists throughout the Nation concerning the directions in which research was needed, and has endeavored to base its programs generally upon this consensus. In addition, where other organizations have undertaken studies of the needs of particular areas of science and have recommended additional support, the Foundation has been in a position to step in with assistance.

That report then cited examples of the variety of experimental programs in science education which the Foundation had initiated, and it described the means used to maintain continuing relationships with the scientific community, both within and outside the Government, and in conclusion, emphasized the importance of the fact that Foundation support is not keyed to a specific agency mission.

Alan T. Waterman's last report as director of the Foundation, in 1963, and Leland J. Haworth's three reports as director, in 1964, 1965, and 1966, are worth careful reading. Dr. Waterman's report, rather than emphasizing the Foundation, consisted of "a review and critical analysis of overall trends in research and development and scientific manpower and the significance these may have for the Nation's strength in science and technology."

Because the Foundation existed in this general situation and was affected by these recent trends, the judgment of its director, after more than a decade in that office, was an important contribution. He stated that the establishment of the Foundation in the immediate postwar period was significant "in its explicit recognition of the critical importance in the overall effort of basic research and education in the sciences."

Dr. Haworth's first report contained his views concerning "the role of science and technology in the life and progress of our country, the responsibilities of the Federal Government for promoting science, technology, and education in the public interest, and, in particular, the role that should be played by the National Science Foundation."

The section on the role of the Foundation contained several statements indicating the new director's views on the subject. The Foundation, as an independent agency of unique characteristics, had been established by Congress with its mission defined in strategic terms, leaving it wide discretion in choosing the mechanisms to be used. The Foundation had wisely chosen to make its approach through stressing the development of the national research capability by using its funds to aid individual research scientists and to strengthen education in the sciences.

In 1965, Dr. Haworth gave the title "The Foundation in Retrospect" to the introductory portion of the annual report. One section dealt with challenges for the future and contained an evaluation of the Foundation's role in circumstances to which its current and future activities must be responsive:

No drastic adjustment is necessary for the Foundation to fit itself comfortably into the altered climate and probable changes in the pattern and direction of support of science and science education. Because of the breadth and flexibility of its legislative mandate, the Foundation is equipped, within limits, to lend its support to research and education for the dual purpose of promoting scientific productivity and providing an opportunity for increased cultural and intellectual development for larger numbers of people. At the same time Foundation activities can both foster and shelter the image of science as a field of intellectual activity that is worthwhile for its own sake.

For this reason, I believe that the Foundation should be regarded, and should think of itself, as the repository of Federal recognition of science as a national resource—a continuously renewable resource that is vital to the national interest. In addition, the Foundation should be the champion and the protector of basic research—the fountainhead of new ideas and the area most likely to suffer in a period of economic retooling of support.

This is not intended to mean that the Foundation can, or should, assume the function of compensating for every change in the pace of support provided by other Federal agencies, nor should it assume the responsibility for doing all the things that others are disinclined to do. On the contrary, with the assistance of the scientific community, the Foundation should assess the total needs, and take advantage of support provided by all other Federal agencies by building upon it when appropriate, and to the extent of available capacity, in order to fulfill total needs as completely as possible.

Near the end of the director's statement this paragraph appeared:

As we look to the years ahead, the Foundation recognizes additional areas of opportunity which now invite exploration. While the picture of the past is satisfying, the years ahead will be years of increasing fulfillment. We must foster and encourage the evolutionary process by which the Foundation has grown, for science is indeed an endless frontier, and we must adapt ourselves to its ever-changing pattern in meeting the continuing challenge.

Dr. Haworth's statement in 1966 dealt primarily with events of that year and their effects on the Foundation and with further objective analysis of the Foundation's goals and programs. The mounting needs of the educational institutions and scientific communities to which it gives support, and the public and official attitudes toward federal support of science and the Foundation's role in pursuit of national goals, were important developments in 1966.

But Dr. Haworth also took time to look to the future, stating:

The National Science Foundation was brought into being largely to assure recognition and support by the Federal Government of the essential place of undirected basic research and of science education in the national scientific effort. The same needs that created the Foundation are even greater today, for an ever-expanding base of scientific innovation and discovery and an ever-increasing pool of scientists and engineers are necessary to preserve the rate of technological advance. For this reason the Foundation, in carrying out its present and any future roles assigned to it for the support of applied research, will always be vigilant in safeguarding its mission to encourage and support basic research.

In carrying out this mission, the Foundation will continue to recognize that research has unusual importance in the context of education, especially graduate education. In addition to the results achieved and to the intellectual stimulus given to the faculty, research is an essential element in the training of advanced students, both because it serves as an apprenticeship for some and because, importantly, it arouses and cultivates in all a spirit of inquiry which will both enrich their lives and enhance their usefulness, whether their ultimate careers be in teaching, research, development, or even other spheres. For it is this spirit of inquiry, of striving always to learn more, that has made for progress in the world, whether it be in science, the humanities, the arts, the technical skills, exploration, or almost any other of man's pursuits.

In Conclusion

Dr. Haworth's paragraphs might well constitute a fitting conclusion not only for this chapter but also for the book as a whole. The Foundation has consistently followed the course laid out in its basic law—"to develop and encourage the pursuit of a national policy for the promotion of basic research and education in the sciences." But the Director's words are official, and to look to an unofficial source may, after all, be more meaningful.

Let us turn again to David Allison, in the pages of *International Science and Technology* (April, 1966):

Visiting the National Science Foundation is a little like making a ceremonial call on a maiden aunt. Nobody says anything unpleasant. Nobody shouts or pounds the table. Tell a member of the Foundation staff that Congressman so-and-so has said an unkind word about him, or about his program, and the NSF man will respond with words of praise for the Congressman.

It is a little odd, this bland, meticulously noncontroversial aura, because the Foundation was conceived in a burst of glory and bitter controversy—and at a time when science was believed by some, and feared by others, to be capable of anything. The time was late in 1944.

How has it worked? I think it fair to say that this strange, bureaucratic invention is turning out to be one of the most important ideas in the history of the country—perhaps as important as the land grant college act of a century ago. Indeed, the early critics were right. It was a revolutionary invention.

Appendix

A Career with the National Science Foundation

The Foundation, with about 1,000 employees, does not, of course, offer anything like the number of career opportunities to be found in the larger departments and agencies that have science and technology functions. Nevertheless, as the size of its staff has increased and it has assumed new functions, and its employees have retired, died, and resigned, the Foundation has over the years made a large number of appointments. These positions have interesting and important duties with good opportunities for professional advancement, and they are particularly suitable for persons who are interested in the public policy aspects of the federal government's science activities.

As is always the case in discussing career opportunities, a first step is to examine the qualifications for the different kinds of jobs required by the employing agency, whether governmental or private. The Office of Naval Research in the Department of Defense, NASA with its space research specialists, the National Institutes of Health, and the Atomic Energy Commission offer quite different opportunities for scientists in their respective, highly specialized fields, and the qualifications for their positions are consequently quite different. The National Science Foundation has few operating programs, and laboratory scientists would not be particularly attracted to the kind of work the Foundation does. To a large extent, the Foundation requires persons with a scientific background joined with the ability to administer its large programs of grants and contracts. Since a very large proportion of these programs is closely related to educational institutions at different levels, an understanding of the needs and the operations of universities and high schools and secondary schools is a valuable qualification. Currently, the Foundation staff includes about 18 per cent of employees with Ph.D.'s, and about half of the staff have professional M.A. or Ph.D. degrees. The minimum requirement for a job at GS-13 or higher is usually an M.A. degree, or more, with experience in teaching or research.

From the lowest grade, GS-2, through GS-13, the Foundation in a recent, typical year had the following number of positions filled: 173 in GS-11, GS-12, and GS-13; 65 in GS-9 and GS-10; 363 in GS-8, GS-7, GS-6, and GS-5; and 118 in GS-4, GS-3, GS-2. The points at which many young people without graduate degrees join the staff of the Foundation are, of course, the lower grades, and the discussion following deals chiefly with career opportunities at these levels.

For the group classified at GS-5 through GS-8, the entering employee is usually a college graduate with a B.A. or B.S. degree, and, since there are usually more applicants than positions, his grades should be B-plus or better. A typical method of application might include these steps, according to a Foundation-published pamphlet:

1. College placement offices, federal postoffices and the local offices of the Civil Service Commission furnish copies of the Application for the Federal Service Entrance Examination, and copies of Standard Form 57, the Standard Application for Federal Employment.
2. When Federal Service Entrance Examinations are held you will receive notice of time, place, and date if you have filed the Application named in (1).
3. After you have taken the examination and passed it, your name will be placed on a list of eligibles from which any Federal agency can make appointments.
4. Form 57 must be filled out and submitted to the agency considering your appointment. This agency can also consider qualified applicants who are not on the list of eligibles.
If you want to work at the National Science Foundation a signed and completed Form 57 must be filed with an NSF representative (if one visits your college campus) or with the Personnel Office, National Science Foundation, 1800 G Street, N.W. Washington, D.C. 20550.

Appointments are made in accordance with the federal civil service laws and regulations and the Classification Act of 1949, although the NSF director may appoint technical and professional personnel without regard to such laws, in cases in which he may deem it necessary.

If a college graduate is appointed to a GS-5 or GS-7 position with the Foundation, he will at first be a trainee in a program designed to give him a broad perspective and understanding of his assignment and its relations to the mission and goals of the Foundation. The following training programs were recently in operation:

Office of Comptroller—accountants and auditors.

Office of Data Management Systems—computer-systems trainees.

Office of Economic Manpower Studies—economists.

Office of Administrative Manager—trainees in personnel, grants, contracts, management analysis, and administrative services.

Grants Office—grants specialists.

Education Division—science-education trainees.

The NSF pamphlet entitled "Career Opportunities with the National Science Foundation" describes each of these trainee programs. The trainee assigned to one of the six offices that carry on trainee programs spends varying amounts of time in the subdivisions of that office. For example, he receives rotational assignments in each of five subdivisions of the Office of the Administrative Manager, giving him training in grants, contracts, management analysis, personnel, and administrative service.

After successful completion of a training program, the employee is assigned to a permanent position and promoted to the next higher grade. Promotional advancement after that depends on the individual's capabilities and available job openings, and it is possible to work up to a GS-11 or GS-12. After that level, the requirement of graduate work enters into qualifications for higher positions. Certain specialized training and employee development programs are offered, particularly in the local universities in Washington, and many government employees continue formal education in the graduate and professional colleges of the Washington universities, which offer for credit toward a degree many such courses in after-work hours. Frequently, employees prepare themselves for promotion by adding an M.A. or a law degree to their entrance qualifications.

Most employees at grades GS-2, GS-3, and GS-4 are in the clerical positions. The Foundation has many good explanatory pamphlets about qualifications, on-the-job training, opportunities for advancement, and other conditions of employment, obtainable from the Office of Personnel in Washington. To be considered, the applicant must have passed the Civil Service examination for typists and stenographers, either locally or in Washington. Complete details and announcements of examinations are available in any post office. There is also a test of verbal abilities and clerical aptitudes. Typists must be able to type forty words per minute, and stenographers must be able to take dictation at eighty words per minute. Appointment to a job is "career-conditional," with civil service status, and this becomes a full "career" appointment after three years. Training opportunities are offered for acquiring skills or knowledge related to the job. There are periodic pay increases for work meeting minimum standards, and special bonuses for unusually high quality performance.

The Foundation recruits applicants for professional positions through representatives who visit university and college campuses. Recruitment for clerical positions is in the Washington area, at high schools, business schools, and two-year colleges which have secretarial courses.

Bibliography

Information concerning the National Science Foundation is to be found in several types of publications. Most useful are the different government publications; also, there are many valuable articles in professional publications such as *Science,* the magazine published by the American Association for the Advancement of Science, and books about science policy and organization.

GOVERNMENT PUBLICATIONS

In the period shortly before and after World War II, among the important reports published were:

Bush, Vannevar. *Science—The Endless Frontier: A Report to the President.* Washington, D.C.: U.S. Gov't. Printing Office, July, 1945. Reprinted in July, 1960, by the National Science Foundation.

U.S. National Resources Committee, Science Committee. *Research—A National Resource.* 3 vols. Washington, D.C.: U.S. Gov't. Printing Office, 1938–41.

U.S. President's Scientific Research Board. John R. Steelman, chairman. *Science and Public Policy.* 5 vols. Washington, D.C.: U.S. Gov't. Printing Office, 1947.

Many reports are published regularly by the National Science Foundation, including annual reports. Several special reports were issued in 1964–65 by the Select Committee on Government Research of the House of Representatives. The Subcommittee on Science, Research, and Development of the House Committee on Science and Astronautics also has published many reports, of which the following are particularly useful in a study of the Foundation:

U.S. Congress, House, Committee on Science and Astronautics, Subcommittee on Science, Research, and Development. *Government and Science: Review of the National Science Foundation: Hearings Before the Subcommittee,* 89th Cong., 1st sess., June, July, August, 1965.

————. *The National Science Foundation: A General Review of Its First 15 Years: Report of the Science Policy Research Division, Legislative Reference Service, Library of Congress,* 89th Cong., 1st sess., 1966, H. Rept. 1219.

————. *The National Science Foundation: Its Present and Future,* 89th Cong., 2d sess., 1966, H. Rept. 1236.

————. *A Bill to Amend the National Science Foundation Act of 1950: Hearings Before the Subcommittee . . . on H.R. 13696, Superseded by H.R. 14838,* 89th Cong., 2d sess., April, 1966.

————. *Amending the National Science Foundation Act of 1950 to Make Improvements in the Organization and Operation of the Foundation,* 89th Cong., 2d sess., 1966, H. Rept. 1650.

————. *Amending the National Science Foundation Act of 1950 to Make Improvements in the Organization and Operation of the Foundation* [to Accompany H.R. 5404], 90th Cong., 1st sess., 1967, H. Rept. 34.

Public materials relating to annual appropriations for the Foundation include the budget of the United States (plus a separate volume presenting special analyses), the hearings in the Senate and the House of Representatives before the subcommittees of the committees on appropriations, the annual appropriation bill and in some years a supplemental appropriation bill, the House report and Senate report, the conference committee report on the bill (sometimes there are more than one of each type), and the final appropriation laws.

Books and Periodicals

Allison, David. "The National Science Foundation." *International Science and Technology,* no. 52, April, 1966, pp. 76–78, 80, 82, 84, 86.

Baldwin, Gordon Brewster. "Law in Support of Science." *Georgetown Law Journal* 54, winter, 1966, pp. 559–91.

Beckler, David. "Strategic Federal Decision-making on R&D." *Research Management* 9, September, 1966, pp. 319–33.

Boffey, Philip M. "Federal Research Funds: Science Gets Caught in a Budget Squeeze." *Science* 158, December 8, 1967, pp. 1286–88.

Carey, William D. "A Rare Glimpse Inside the Budget Bureau." *Scientific Research* 2, July, 1967, pp. 29–31.

Daddario, Emilio Q. "A Revised Charter for the Science Foundation." *Science* 152, April 1, 1966, pp. 42–45.

DuBridge, Lee A. "University Basic Research." *Science* 157, August 11, 1967, pp. 648–50.

Dupré, J. Stefan, and Lakoff, Sanford A. *Science and the Nation: Policy and Politics.* Englewood Cliffs, N.J.: Prentice-Hall, 1962.

Dupree, A. Hunter. *Science in the Federal Government: A History of Policies and Activities to 1940.* Cambridge, Mass.: Harvard Univ. Press, Belknap Press, 1957.

Gilpin, Robert, and Wright, Christopher, eds. *Scientists and National Policy-making.* New York: Columbia Univ. Press, 1964. See particularly Christopher Wright, "Scientists and the Establishment of Science Affairs," pp. 257–302.

Greenberg, D. S. "Daddario Study Says NSF Should Be in Forefront of Policymaking." *Science* 151, January 14, 1966, pp. 177–79.

————. "Money for NSF: The Odyssey of a Research Agency's Budget." *Science* 157, October 20, 1967, pp. 357–61.

————. "The Administration of Federal Aid: A Monstrosity Has Been Created." *Science* 157, July 7, 1967, pp. 43–47.

————. "The Politics of Pure Science." *Saturday Review* 50, November 4, 1967, pp. 62–69.

Handler, Philip. "Academic Science and the Federal Government." *Science* 157, September 8, 1967, pp. 1140–46.

————. "Federal Science Policy: Roles of the President's Science Advisory Committee and the National Science Board." *Science* 155, March 3, 1967, pp. 1063–66.

Hornig, Donald F. "Thinking Ahead . . . with Donald Hornig. On Planning Science." *International Science and Technology*, no. 49, January, 1966, pp. 66–70.

Keenan, Boyd R., ed. *Science and the University*. New York: Columbia Univ. Press, 1966.

Lear, John. "Einstein's Angel and the Empty Temple." *Saturday Review* 50, April 1, 1967, pp. 45–46.

Price, Don K. *Government and Science: Their Dynamic Relation in American Democracy*. New York: New York Univ. Press, 1954.

————. *The Scientific Estate*. Cambridge, Mass.: Harvard Univ. Press, Belknap Press, 1965.

Science, Government, and the Universities. Seattle: Univ. of Washington Press, 1966.

"$200 Million in Pursuit of Excellence—Science Agencies Hope to Make Good Colleges Better, Better Ones Best." *Scientific Research* 1, June, 1966, pp. 10–12.

Walker, Eric A. "National Science Board: Its Place in National Policy." *Science* 156, April 28, 1967, pp. 474–77.

————. "Research: Vexatious Issues Between Government and University." *Science* 155, March 24, 1967, pp. 1489–90.

Walsh, John. "Demand for Institutional Support Attains the Form of Legislation." *Science* 152, May 20, 1966, pp. 1041–43.

————. "International Science Activities: Some New Vistas Open." *Science* 152, June 17, 1966, pp. 1605–7.

Waterman, Alan T. "Federal Support of Science." *Science* 153, September 16, 1966, pp. 1351–61.

————. "The National Science Foundation: A Ten-Year Resumé." *Science* 131, May 6, 1960, pp. 1341–54.

Weinberg, Alvin M. *Reflections on Big Science*. Cambridge, Mass.: MIT Press, 1967.

Wolfle, Dael. "National Science Foundation: The First Six Years." *Science* 126, August 23, 1957, pp. 335–43.

Index